Ramp-Up to Algebra

Geometry and Measure

AMERICA'S
CHOICE®

Acknowledgments

Authors:

America's Choice® developed and field-tested Ramp-Up to Algebra over a ten-year period. Initial development started with a grant from the Office of Educational Research and Improvement (OERI) of the U.S. Department of Education, and was based on the most recent research in mathematics. During that ten-year period many authors, reviewers, and math consultants—both from the United States and internationally—contributed to this course. The materials underwent three major revisions as we analyzed field-test results and consulted math content experts. During the entire time, Phil Daro guided the development of the entire Ramp-Up to Algebra curriculum. See the *Getting Started* Teacher Resource guide for a complete list of people involved in this effort.

America's Choice® is a subsidiary of the National Center on Education and the Economy® (NCEE), a Washington, DC-based non-profit organization and a leader in standards-based reform. In the late 1990s, NCEE launched the America's Choice School Design, a comprehensive, standards-based, school-improvement program that serves students through partnerships with states, school districts, and schools nationwide. In addition to the school design, America's Choice provides instructional systems in literacy, mathematics, and school leadership. Consulting services are available to help school leaders build strategies for raising student performance on a large scale.

ISBN 978-1-60637-716-1

Printed in China
First Printing, 2009
1 2 3 4 5 6 7 8 9 10   13 12 11 10 09

www.americaschoice.org
products@americaschoice.org
800.221.3641

Table of Contents

Angles, Lines, and Constructions

Two-Dimensional Figures: Angles

Table of Contents

Table of Contents

Table of Contents

Table of Contents

Three-Dimensional Figures: Measurements and Constructions

Table of Contents

Three-Dimensional Figures: Measurements and Constructions (continued)

MATH
AT
WORK

LINES AND ANGLES

GOAL

To name and distinguish lines, rays, and line segments; to identify and name angles and compare their sizes.

Lines, Rays, and Segments

Lines are straight, one-dimensional objects that keep going, without end, in both directions.

The two figures at right shows examples of lines. The arrows mean that they keep going in each direction without end.

You write $\overleftrightarrow{AB}$ for the line through points A and B—or just a lower case letter l.

Any number of lines can pass through a single point A. There is only one line that passes through both points A and B. If a third point, C, is on the line AB, then line AC is just another name for line AB.

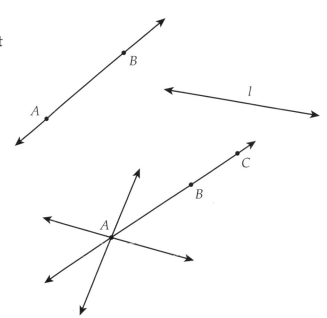

A *ray* is part of a line. A ray starts at one endpoint and goes on forever in one direction only. Using two given points, A and B, you can draw two different rays.

This is a ray with endpoint at B. The arrow means that the ray keeps going on past point A without end.

You write $\overrightarrow{BA}$ for this ray.

This is a different ray.

You write $\overrightarrow{AB}$ for this ray from A through B.

A part of a line that has two endpoints is called a *line segment*. Line segments are drawn without arrows on either end. The figure at right shows line segments.

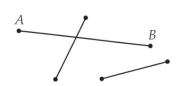

You write $\overline{AB}$ to refer to the line segment with endpoints A and B.

Angles

Two rays or line segments with one common endpoint form an *angle*. The common endpoint is called the *vertex* of the angle, and the line segments or rays form the sides of the angle.

CONCEPT BOOK

See page 216.

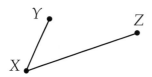

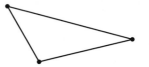

These line segments form an angle with a vertex at point X. $\overline{XY}$ and $\overline{XZ}$ can also be referred to as the *arms* of angle X.

These two rays form a straight angle.

The line segments of a triangle form three angles.

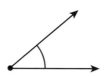

An angle that measures less than 90° is called an *acute* angle.

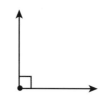

An angle that measures exactly 90° is called a *right* angle.

An angle that measures more than 90° and less than 180° is called an *obtuse* angle.

An angle that measures exactly 180° is called a *straight* angle.

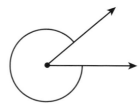

An angle that measures more than 180° and less than 360° is called a *reflex* angle.

Intersecting lines, rays, or segments can form more than one angle.

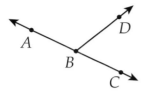

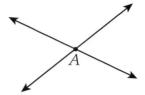

Not counting the reflex angles, this figure has three angles: ∠DBC, ∠ABC, and ∠ABD.

These two intersecting lines form six angles, each with their vertex at the point of intersection.

> **Comment**
>
> The symbol ∠ means angle.

Angles are named using letters to indicate three points on the angle—one point on each side, and one point at the vertex. If there is no possibility of confusion, angles can be named using only the vertex point.

> **Comment**
>
> As a general guideline, you do not need to be concerned with reflex angles unless they are specifically called out or identified as such.

Here there is only one angle that has a vertex at A. This is an acute angle that can be called ∠A, ∠BAC, or ∠CAB.

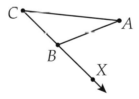

There are several angles that have a vertex at B, so you need to use three letters to distinguish the angles. The obtuse angle is called ∠ABC or ∠CBA. The acute angle is called ∠ABX or ∠XBA.

There are several different names that could be used for the angle with a vertex at C. Apart from ∠C, you could also write ∠ACB, ∠ACX, ∠BCA, or ∠XCA.

Work Time

1. Here are fifteen different figures made from rays, lines, and line segments.

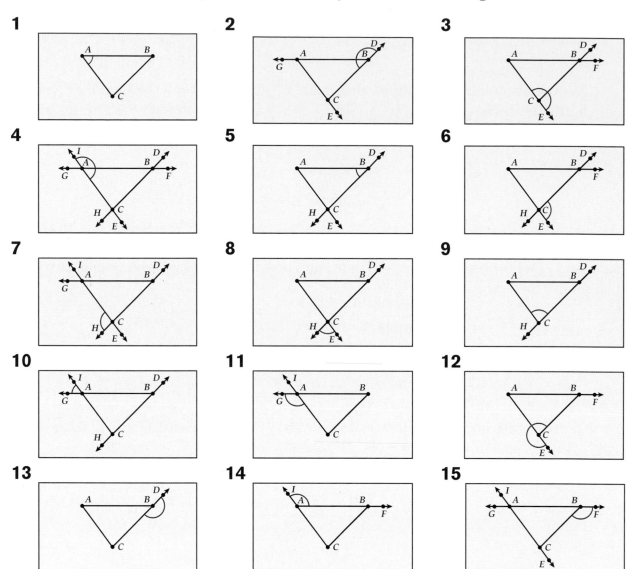

On the next page you will see a table that describes these figures. Work with a partner to copy and complete this table. For each description identify:

- Which figure matches the description
- The lines, rays, and line segments that make up the figure
- One name that the angle indicated by an arc, △, could be called
- The classification of the indicated angle (acute, obtuse, straight, or reflex)

	Description	Figure	Lines, Rays, and Segments	Name for Angle	Type of Angle
a.	The figure with three line segments	1	$\overline{AB}, \overline{BC}, \overline{AC}$	$\angle A$	Acute
b.	The figure with three lines				
c.	The figure with three rays with three different endpoints				
d.	The other figure with three rays				
e.	The figure with two line segments and one line				
f.	The figure with two line segments and one ray				
g.	The figure with two lines and one line segment				
h.	The figure with two lines and one ray				
i.	The figure with one line and two rays from the same endpoint				
j.	The figure with one line and two rays from different endpoints				
k.	The two identical figures				
l.	The figure with one line segment and two rays from the same endpoint				
m.	The figure with a line segment with rays from each of its endpoints				
n.	The one remaining figure				

Preparing for the Closing

2. Discuss your answers with your partner. Look for different ways to name the angles, lines, and rays.

3. Lisa said that figure 3 has three rays. Dwayne said that figure 3 has three rays along with three line segments. Who is right? Explain why.

Skills

Calculate.

a. $250 + 83 - 50 =$

b. $195 + 43 - 95 =$

c. $180 - 54 - 53 =$

d. $340 - 42 + 60 - 58 =$

e. $360 - 36 - 54 =$

f. $180 + 20 + 35 =$

Review and Consolidation

1. Work with a partner to copy and complete this table. For each figure:

   • Write how many angles are in the figure (not counting straight or reflex angles).

   • Write all possible names for the angle marked by an arc, $\triangle$.

   • Name the smallest and largest angles (not counting straight or reflex angles).

   • Name the three lines, line segments, and/or rays that form the figure.

Figure	How Many Angles?	Names for Marked Angle	Smallest and Largest Angles	Names of Three Lines or Rays
a. 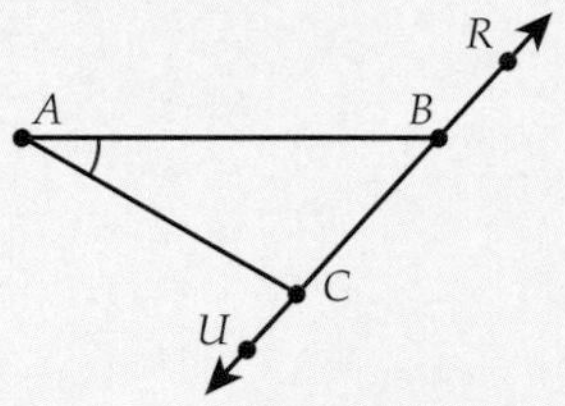				
b. 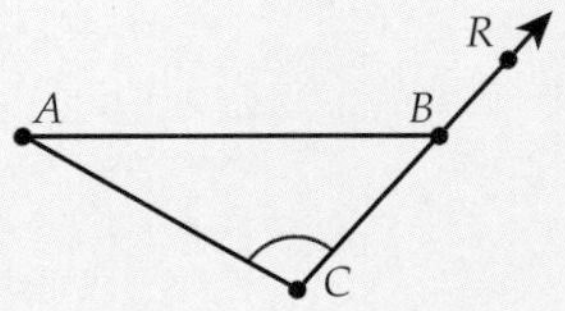				

Figure	How Many Angles?	Names for Marked Angle	Smallest and Largest Angles	Names of Three Lines or Rays
c.				
d.				
e.				
f.				
g.				

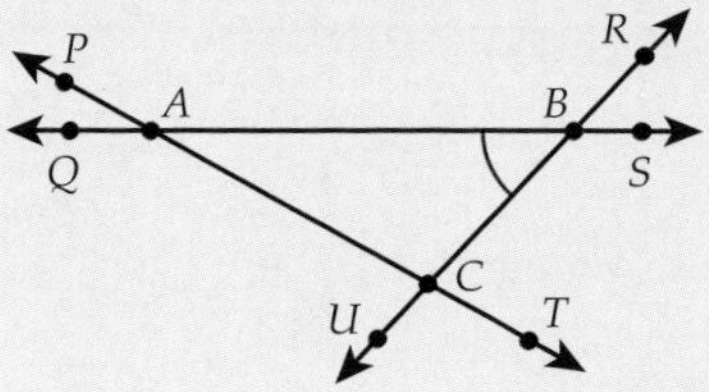

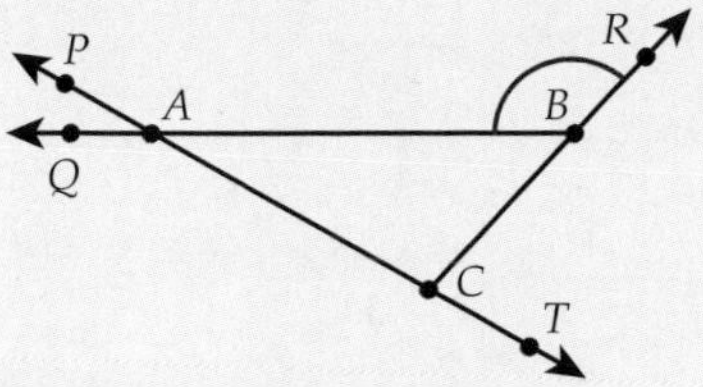

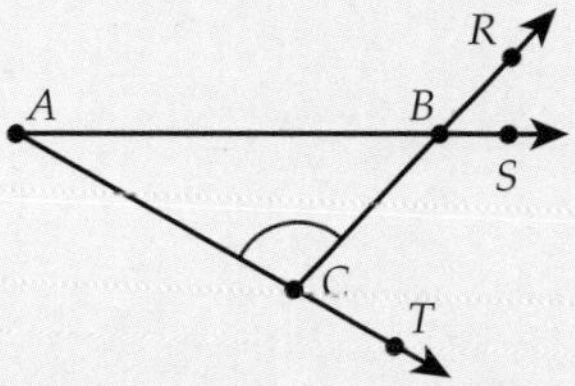

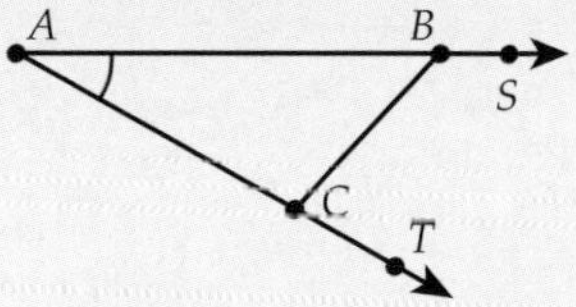

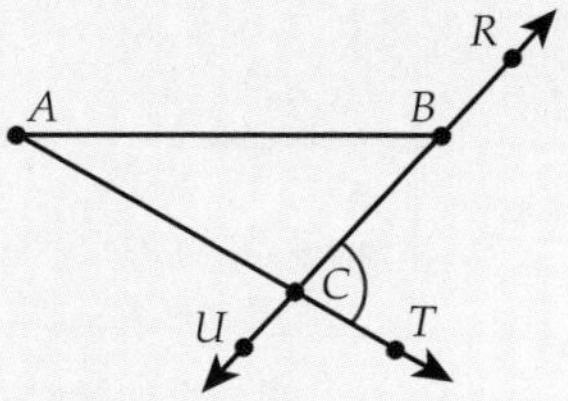

Homework

1. a. Rosa said that this figure has two rays
      and two lines. Jamal said that the figure
      has six line segments and six rays.
      Explain why both students are correct.

   b. Eight line segments can be found in the figure.
      Name them.

   c. What type of angle is marked at B?

   d. Name the angle that is marked at B.

   e. What type of angle is marked at C?

   f. What type of angle is marked at D?

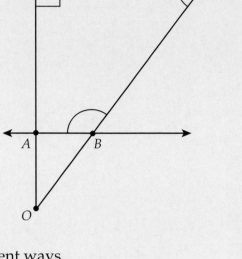

   g. Name the angle that is marked at D in four different ways.

2. a. How many straight angles are there in this figure?
      Name them.

   b. Name all the other angles in the figure.
      Write them in order from smallest to largest.

   c. One of the angles in the figure can be named as
      ∠CGY. Write at least four other ways of naming
      this same angle, including the simplest way.

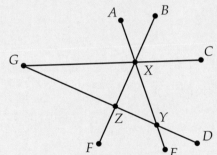

ANGLES AT A VERTEX

GOAL

To review angle measure, and to identify vertical (or vertically opposite) angles, adjacent angles, supplementary angles, and complementary angles.

The angles that form a complete circle around any one vertex have a total measure of 360°.

CONCEPT BOOK

See pages 216–217.

Example

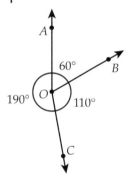

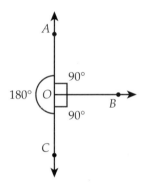

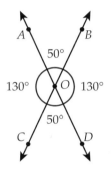

Here, the 360° is made up of an acute angle of 60°, an obtuse angle of 110°, and a reflex angle, ∠AOC, of 190°.

The 360° is made up of a straight angle and two right angles.

Two intersecting lines create four angles.

Each pair of equal angles are *vertically opposite angles* or *vertical angles*

$$60° + 110° + 190° = 360°$$ $$180° + 90° + 90° = 360°$$ $$50° + 130° + 50° + 130° = 360°$$

Adjacent angles are angles that are next to each other, and that have one side in common. In the vertical angles example above, ∠AOB is adjacent to ∠BOC, with common side $\overline{OB}$. In contrast, ∠AOB is not adjacent to ∠COD.

In rectangle ABCD, ∠ABC is adjacent to ∠BCD, with common side $\overline{BC}$, but ∠ABC is not adjacent to ∠CDA. Note that adjacent angles do not always have the same vertex: ∠ABC is adjacent to ∠BCD, but these angles have different vertices.

Supplementary angles are angles with measures that add up to 180°. In other words, supplementary angles together form a straight angle. There are pairs of supplementary angles in the rectangle and in two of the three example figures on the preceding page. Can you find them?

Complementary angles are angles with measures that add up to 90°. In other words, complementary angles together form a right angle. In this figure, x and y are complementary angles.

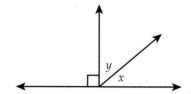

Work Time

1. Keesha has made common mistakes in measuring the angles in the figures below.

   Use your protractor to find the correct measurements. In each case, write advice for Keesha about the mistake and how to avoid making it.

a.

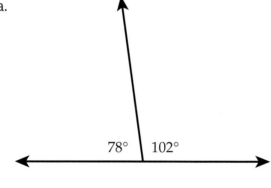

78°   102°

b.

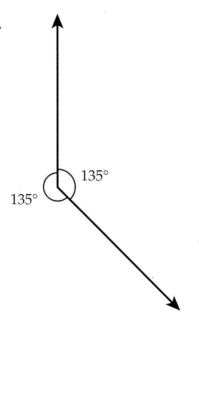

135°

135°

c.

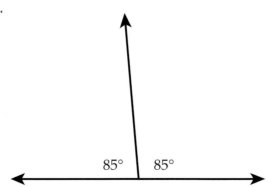

85°   85°

2. Measure the angles in this figure as accurately as possible, and check that they add up to 360°.

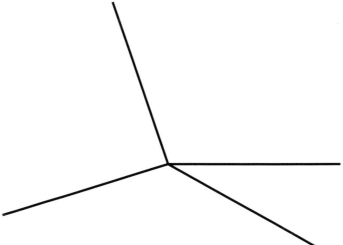

3. For the figure shown at right:

a. Write an equation using the angle measures, and calculate the value of angle x.

b. How many pairs of vertical angles are there?

c. How many pairs of supplementary angles are there?

d. How many straight angles are there?

e. There are four angles adjacent to angle x. What are the measures of these angles?

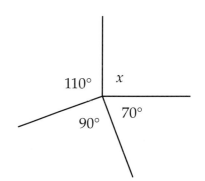

4. The figure shown at right has three intersecting lines:

a. Calculate the values of angles w, x, y, and z.

b. How many pairs of vertical angles are there?

c. How many pairs of complementary angles are there?

d. How many pairs of supplementary angles are there?

e. How many right angles are there?

f. How many straight angles are there?

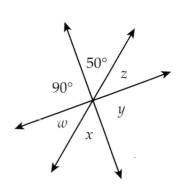

Preparing for the Closing

5. Discuss your answers to problems 1 and 2 with your partner. Together, make a list of the most common errors made when measuring angles with a protractor.

6. Sketch a figure of three angles around a vertex that matches the equation $x + 2x + 84° = 360°$. Calculate the measure of each angle.

7. Explain why vertical angles are equal.

8. Classify the following as *always true*, *sometimes true*, or *never true*.

   a. Adjacent angles are supplementary.

   b. Adjacent angles are complementary.

   c. Adjacent angles have a common side and a common vertex.

   d. Vertical angles are supplementary.

   e. The measure of an angle is greater than its reflex measure.

Skills

Solve.

   a. $180 - 50 - 40 = \rule{1em}{0.8em}$

   b. $180 - 65 - 40 = \rule{1em}{0.8em}$

   c. $180 - 65 - \rule{1em}{0.8em} = 90$

   d. $45 + 60 + 97 + 158 = \rule{1em}{0.8em}$

   e. $180 + 95 + \rule{1em}{0.8em} = 360$

   f. $127 + 53 + 127 + \rule{1em}{0.8em} = 360$

Review and Consolidation

1. For the figure shown below:

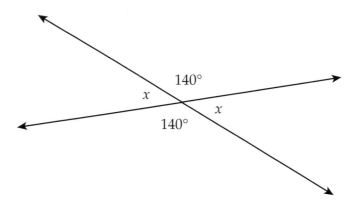

a. Write an equation using the angle measures, and calculate the value of x.

b. How many pairs of vertical angles are there?

c. How many pairs of supplementary angles are there?

d. How many straight angles are there?

e. What is the sum of the measures of any two adjacent angles?

2. Sketch a figure, different from the one above, that also matches the equation $x + x + 140° + 140° = 360°$.

For this new figure:

a. How many pairs of vertical angles are there?

b. How many pairs of supplementary angles are there?

c. How many straight angles are there?

d. Write the sum of the measures for each pair of adjacent angles.

3. Make up a figure like the one in problem 1, but label your figure incorrectly. Give it to your partner to correct.

1. The figure at right has three intersecting lines.

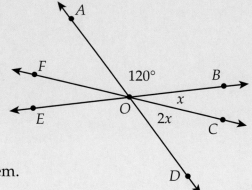

a. Write an equation and calculate the value of x.

b. How many pairs of vertical angles are there? Name them.

c. How many pairs of supplementary angles are there? Name them.

d. How many straight angles are there? Name them.

2. This figure shows an equilateral triangle and one of its exterior angles.

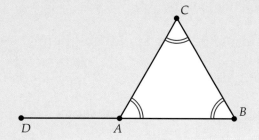

a. Name the straight angle.

b. Name a pair of adjacent supplementary angles.

c. Name a pair of angles that are supplementary, but not adjacent.

d. Which line segment would have to be extended in order to create two pairs of vertical angles?

CORRESPONDING ANGLES AND ALTERNATE ANGLES

GOAL

To identify pairs of corresponding angles and pairs of alternate angles, and to determine when the angles are congruent.

Angles on Intersecting Lines

When one line intersects two other lines, eight angles are created.

In the figure at right:

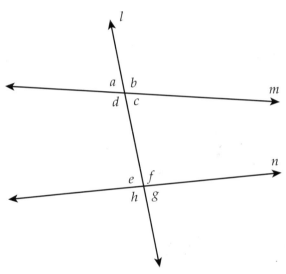

- Line l is called the *transversal* of lines m and n.

- Angles d and f are called a pair of *alternate angles,* or *alternate interior angles.* They are in the area between the lines m and n, and on opposite (or alternate) sides of the transversal l.

- Angles c and e are a second pair of alternate angles.

- Angles a and e are called a pair of *corresponding angles.* They lie in corresponding positions at the two intersections (top left of the intersections in the figure).

- Angles b and f are a second pair of corresponding angles (top right at the intersections).

- Angles c and g are a third pair of corresponding angles (bottom right at the intersections).

- Angles d and h are a fourth pair of corresponding angles (bottom left at the intersections).

In this figure, lines *m* and *n* are parallel to each other, and are marked with the symbol ➤. If this symbol is not shown in a figure, you cannot assume that lines are parallel.

Here, the eight angles are made up of four equal acute angles, *x*, and four equal obtuse angles, $y = 180° - x$.

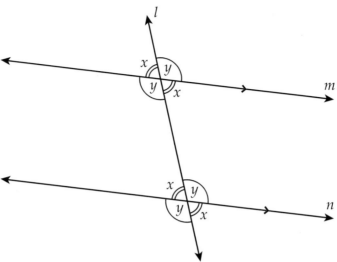

If lines *m* and *n* are parallel, then alternate angles have equal measure and are said to be *congruent*.

If lines *m* and *n* are parallel, then corresponding angles are also congruent.

Work Time

1. In the figure at right, angle *c* is one angle in a pair of alternate angles.

    a. Which is the other angle in the pair?

    b. Which angles make up the other pair of alternate angles?

    c. Alternate angles are found in the area between lines *m* and *n*. What is specific about their relation to the transversal *l*?

    d. How does the word "alternate" help describe which angles make up a pair of alternate angles?

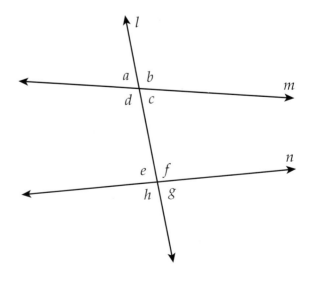

2. In this figure, $f = 95°$ and lines m and n form angle x where they intersect at point R.

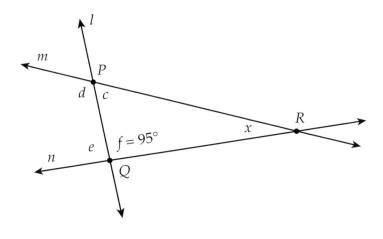

a. In triangle PQR, if $x = 15°$, then:

   i. How does the value of d compare to that of its alternate angle f?

   ii. How does the value of c compare to that of its alternate angle e?

b. Now imagine line m rotating counterclockwise about point P so that point R moves further away along line n.

   i. Would the value of angle d become closer to $95°$ or further away from $95°$? Explain your answer.

   ii. Would the values of angles c and e become closer to each other or further away from each other? Explain your answer.

   iii. If point R moved an infinite distance to the right along line n, then lines m and n would be parallel. How would this affect the values of c, d, and e?

3. In this figure, $f = 75°$ and lines m and n again form angle x where they intersect at point R.

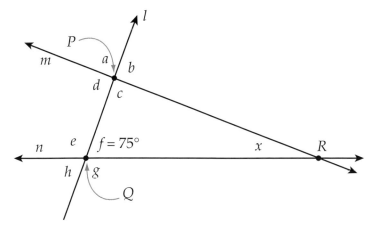

a. In triangle PQR, if $x = 15°$, then:

   i. How does the value of b compare to that of its corresponding angle f?

   ii. How does the value of c compare to that of its corresponding angle g?

   iii. Name two other pairs of corresponding angles.

   iv. What is the difference in measure between the angles in each of these pairs of corresponding angles?

b. Now imagine line *m* rotating counterclockwise about point *P* so that point *R* moves further to the right along line *n*.

    i.   Would the value of angle *b* become closer to 75° or further away from 75°? Explain your answer.

    ii. Would the values of angles *c* and *g* become closer to each other or further away from each other? Explain your answer.

    iii. If point *R* moved an infinite distance to the right along line *n*, then lines *m* and *n* would be parallel. How would this affect the values of the corresponding angles?

4. In the figures below, some lines are parallel and others are not. The measures of several angles are also given. Where possible, find the measures of the angles identified. Give reasons for your answers.

a.

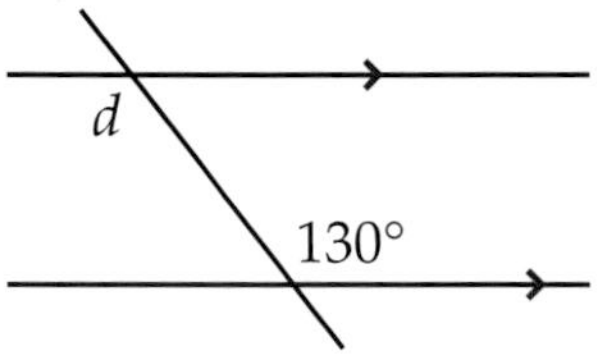

b.

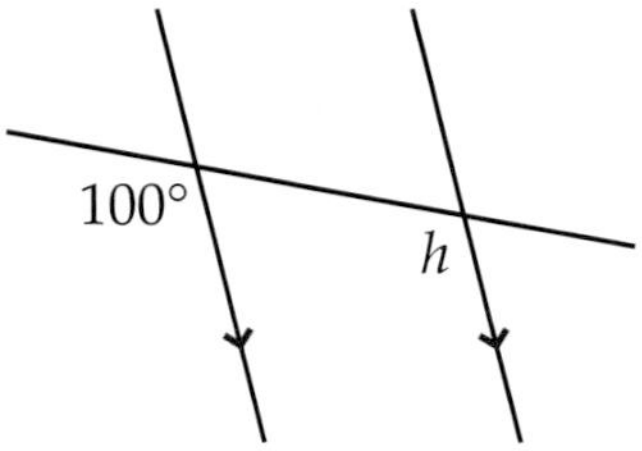

c.

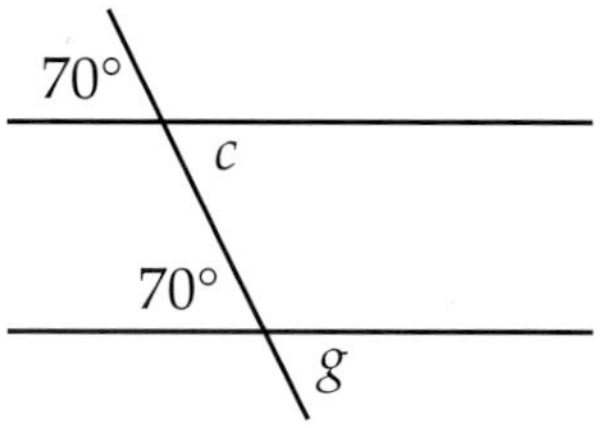

d.

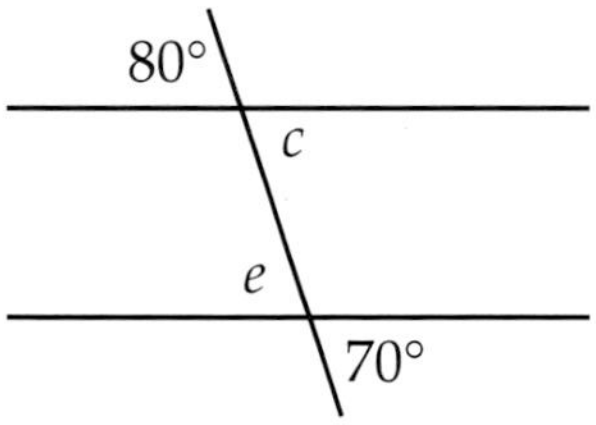

e.

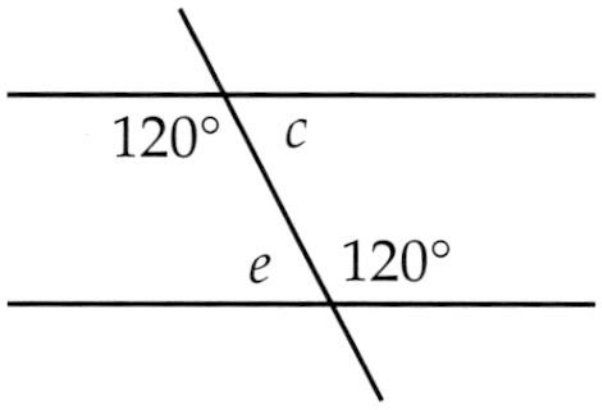

f.

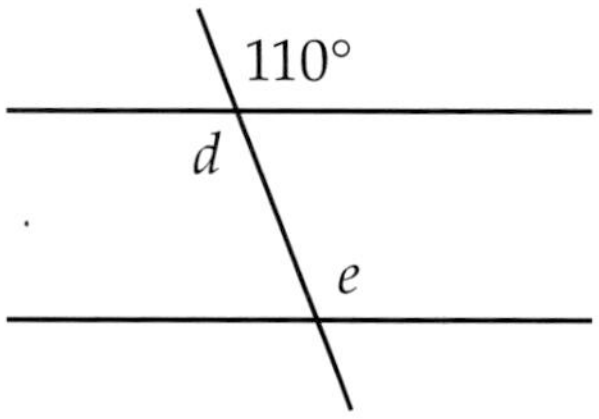

Preparing for the Closing

5. Look again at the figures in problem 4.

a. For which of the six figures can you be certain that there is a pair of parallel lines? Say why.

b. For which of the six figures can you be certain that there is no pair of parallel lines? Say why.

c. For which of the six figures is there insufficient information for you to decide whether or not there is a pair of parallel lines?

6. Classify each of the following statements as *always true*, *sometimes true*, or *never true*. Give reasons for your answers.

a. If two lines are parallel, then corresponding angles are equal.

b. If two lines are parallel, then alternate angles are equal.

c. If two lines are intersected by a third line, then four pairs of congruent corresponding angles are created.

d. If the angles in at least one pair of alternate angles are equal, then the lines containing them are parallel.

e. If the angles in at least one pair of corresponding angles are equal, then two of the lines creating them are parallel.

f. If the sum of the angles in a pair of alternate angles is 180°, then the lines containing them are parallel.

Skills

Solve.

a. $0.10 = ▢ ¢

b. $0.20 = ▢ ¢

c. $0.50 = ▢ ¢

d. $1.00 = ▢ ¢

e. $1 = ▢ ¢

f. $2 = ▢ ¢

g. $5 = ▢ ¢

h. $10 = ▢ ¢

i. $1.25 = ▢ ¢

j. $1.05 = ▢ ¢

k. $20.05 = ▢ ¢

l. $2.20 = ▢ ¢

Review and Consolidation

1. Sketch a figure that shows a pair of alternate angles on lines that are not parallel. Label the degree measures of each angle, with one of the angles labeled as 50°.

2. Sketch a figure that shows a pair of corresponding angles on parallel lines. Label one of the angles as 150° and calculate the size of the other angle.

3. Explain why there are two pairs of parallel lines in the figure at right.

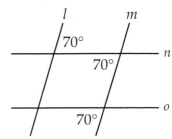

1. For the figure at right:

    a. Name the two pairs of alternate angles.

    b. Name the four pairs of corresponding angles.

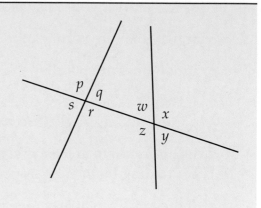

2. Find the values of angles *x* and *y* in the following figures. Give reasons for your answers.

    a.

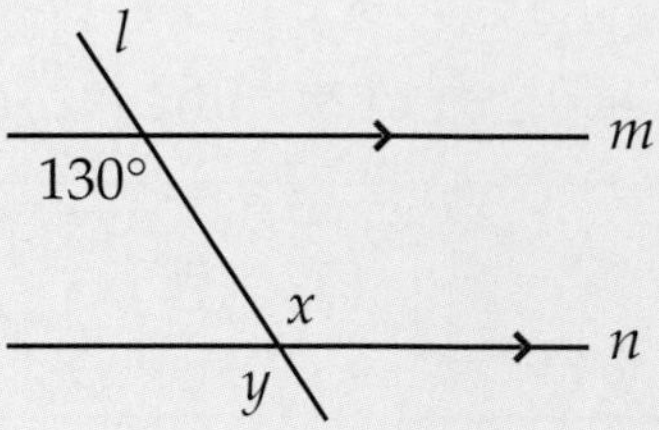

    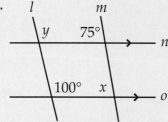

    b.

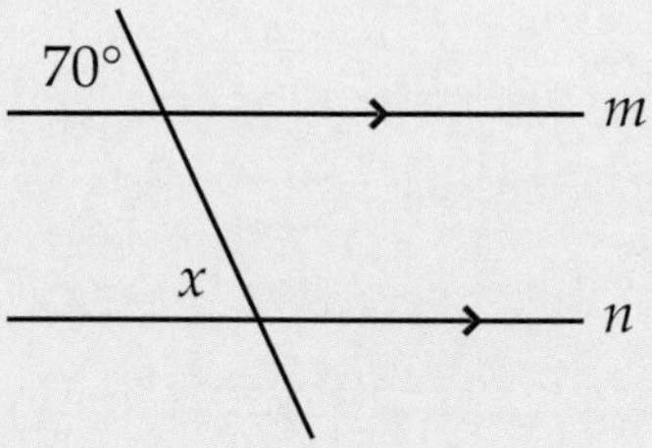

    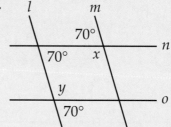

    c.

    d.

3. Refer to the figures in problem 2. Name the pairs of parallel lines in each figure, and say how you know that they are parallel.

4. Write a short summary of what you know about pairs of alternate angles and corresponding angles on parallel lines. Include figures as part of your summary.

CONSTRUCTING ANGLE BISECTORS

GOAL

To bisect angles using a straightedge and compass.

A ray that divides an angle into two equal parts is called the *bisector* of that angle.

If you let ray *OC* be a bisector of ∠*AOB*, then:

$$\angle AOC = \angle BOC = \frac{1}{2} \angle AOB$$

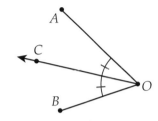

Example

Here is a step-by-step guide to constructing the bisector of an angle using a compass and a straightedge.

Step 1 Using a straightedge, draw an acute angle *AOB*.

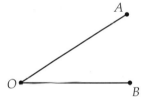

Step 2 Draw a circle using the vertex of ∠*AOB*, point *O*, as the center. Label the points where the circle intersects with the sides *OA* and *OB* of the angle as points *C* and *D*.

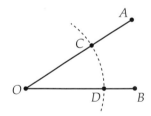

Step 3 Construct two circles of equal radii with points *C* and *D* as their respective centers. Label one point of intersection for the two circles as point *E*.

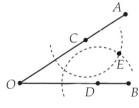

Step 4 Draw the ray *OE*. $\overrightarrow{OE}$ is the bisector of ∠*AOB*.

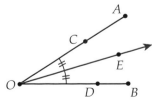

Work Time

1. a. Use a straightedge to create an acute angle. Then, use a compass to bisect the angle, following steps 2, 3, and 4 from the example on the previous page.

   b. Use a straightedge to create an obtuse angle. Then, use a compass to bisect the angle.

   c. Verify that you have bisected each angle correctly by measuring the resulting angles with a protractor to make sure that they are equal.

2. Work with a partner. Decide who will start with an acute triangle, and who will start with an obtuse angle.

   a. Work separately to make a geometric construction starting with your chosen angle. Make sure your partner does not see your work!

   - Create a figure that contains at least two bisected angles.

   - You may add any letters or lines, rays, or segments that you want.

   - You must be able to describe how to create your construction in no more than six steps.

   b. Write instructions of no more than six steps about how to make your construction.

   ┌ Example ──────────────────────────────

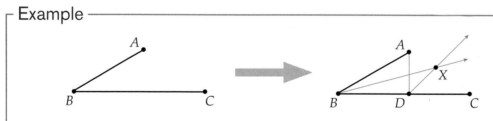

1	Use a compass and ruler to create the bisector of ∠ABC.
2	Draw any line down from point A to the line BC.
3	Mark the point where this line touches the line BC as D.
4	Use a compass and ruler to create the bisector of ∠ADC.
5	Mark the intersection of the two bisectors as point X.

   c. Swap instructions with your partner.

   d. Now follow your partner's instructions to recreate your partner's construction. Do not look at your partner's figure until you have finished all the steps.

Preparing for the Closing

3. Compare the figure you made using your partner's instructions with the one that your partner made. Discuss any differences with your partner.

Skills

Calculate.

a. $2.50 – $0.92 + $0.52 =

b. $13.74 + $0.38 – $0.54 – $0.20 =

c. $0.27 + $4.38 – $0.38 =

d. $16.83 + $12.38 – $14.83 =

e. $12.56 + $7.42 – $0.06 =

f. $38.56 + $25.74 – $12.73 =

Review and Consolidation

1. a. Draw a large triangle of any kind on a full sheet of paper. Label the vertices *A*, *B*, and *C*.

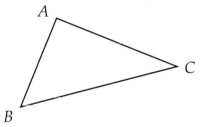

b. Use a compass and straightedge to construct the angle bisectors of all three angles of the triangle. If you do this accurately, all three of the bisectors will intersect at the same point. Label this point as *X*.

c. Use a compass to construct a circle with center at *X*. Adjust the radius so that the circle touches one side of the triangle.

d. Explain why the circle is called an *inscribed circle*.

Homework

1. a. Draw a large rectangle on a full sheet of paper. Make sure that all four angles are 90°. Starting in the upper left corner, label the four vertices as *A*, *B*, *C*, and *D*.

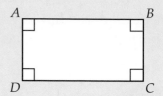

   b. Use a compass and straightedge to construct the angle bisectors of all four angles of your rectangle. If you do this accurately, the bisectors will intersect at four distinct points. Label the topmost intersection point *S*, and label the bottommost point *T*.

   c. Use a straightedge to draw a line through *S* and *T* that intersects the rectangle twice. Label the top point of intersection *E* and the bottom point *F*.

   d. What do you notice about the line segment *EF* and the figures *AEFD* and *EBCF*?

2. What do you suppose would be the result if you performed the steps above on a square instead of a rectangle?

CONSTRUCTING PERPENDICULAR BISECTORS

GOAL

To construct the perpendicular bisector of a line segment using a straightedge and compass, and to construct a line perpendicular to a line segment through a point not on the line segment.

A line at 90° to another line that cuts that line into two equal parts is called the *perpendicular bisector* of the line.

If you let $\overleftrightarrow{CD}$ be the perpendicular bisector of $\overline{AB}$, then:

$$\overline{AE} = \overline{EB} = \frac{1}{2}\overline{AB}$$

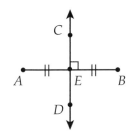

Example

Here is a step-by-step guide for constructing the perpendicular bisector of a line segment using a compass and a straightedge.

Step 1 Using a straightedge, draw a line segment AB.

Step 2 Using a compass, draw two circles of equal radii with centers at points A and B. Let the points C and D be the intersections of these two circles.

Step 3 Draw the line CD.

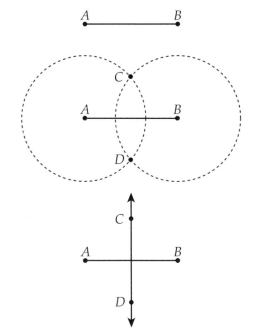

What if you want to draw a perpendicular line through a given point?

Example

Here are the steps for constructing a perpendicular line from any point.

Start with a point C not on a line.

C •

Step 1   Using a compass, draw a circle with center C that intersects the line at two points. Label these points A and B.

Step 2   Without adjusting the compass setting, follow steps 2 and 3 of the previous example to draw line segment CD.

Work Time

1. a. Use a straightedge to draw a line segment AB. Then, use the straightedge and a compass to construct the perpendicular bisector of segment AB.

  b. Verify that you have constructed the perpendicular bisector correctly by measuring the resulting angles with a protractor to make sure that they are equal, and the resulting lengths with a ruler to make sure that they are equal.

2. a. Use a straightedge to draw a line AB and then mark a point C not on the line. Using a compass and straightedge, construct a perpendicular line to $\overline{AB}$ that passes through point C.

  b. Verify that you have a perpendicular line by measuring the resulting angles with a protractor to make sure that they are equal.

3. Follow these instructions, but do not show your construction to your partner until you are both finished.

    a. Construct a triangle with side lengths 10 cm, 9 cm, and 7 cm by doing the following:

- Start by using a ruler to draw a line segment AB of length 10 cm.
- Using a compass, draw an arc of radius 9 cm using one endpoint of $\overline{AB}$ as center.
- Using a compass, draw an arc of radius 7 cm using the other endpoint as center.
- Label the point where the arcs intersect C. This is the third vertex of your triangle.
- Using a straightedge, draw in sides $\overline{AC}$ and $\overline{BC}$ of the triangle.

    b. Construct the perpendicular bisector for each of the three sides of the triangle: $\overline{AB}$, $\overline{BC}$, and $\overline{AC}$.

    c. Find the point where the three perpendicular bisectors intersect. Label this point X.

Preparing for the Closing

4. a. On the construction above, use your compass to draw a circle of radius AX with point X as its center.

    b. What do you observe?

Skills

Calculate.

    a. $15(3 + 4) =$ b. $27(3 + 8) =$ c. $148(12 - 5) =$

    d. $15(13 + 4) =$ e. $27(13 + 8) =$ f. $148(22 - 5) =$

    g. $15(23 + 4) =$ h. $27(23 + 8) =$ i. $148(32 - 5) =$

Review and Consolidation

1. Follow these instructions, but do not show your construction to your partner until you are both finished.

   a. Draw a line segment *AC* of length 6.0 cm.

   b. Construct the perpendicular bisector of $\overline{AC}$.

   c. Label the point where the perpendicular bisector intersects $\overline{AC}$ as point *X*.

   d. Using a compass, draw a circle of radius *AX* with point *X* as its center.

   e. Label the points where the circle intersects the perpendicular bisector as points *B* and *D*.

   f. Use a straightedge to construct the square *ABCD*.

   g. Use a ruler and a protractor to measure how accurate you were in each construction.

Homework

1. a. Construct a right triangle *ABC* by doing the following:

   - Draw a line *XY* and a mark a point *A* that is not on the line.

   - Using a compass and straightedge, construct a perpendicular line from point *A* to $\overleftrightarrow{XY}$. Label the point where the perpendicular line intersects $\overleftrightarrow{XY}$ as point *B*.

   - Draw a line segment from *A* to any other point on $\overleftrightarrow{XY}$ other than *B*. Call this point *C*.

   b. Construct the perpendicular bisector for each of the three sides of the triangle: $\overline{AB}$, $\overline{BC}$, and $\overline{AC}$.

   c. Find the point where the three perpendicular bisectors intersect. Label this point *Z*.

   d. What do you observe about the point *Z*?

QUADRILATERALS

GOAL

To define quadrilaterals, and to understand special types of quadrilaterals, especially the rectangle.

A *quadrilateral* is a four-sided, closed, plane figure.

What does "closed" mean?

Closed means that the area within the figure is completely enclosed.

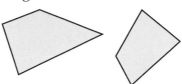

CONCEPT BOOK

See pages 227–229.

What does "plane figure" mean?

A *plane figure* lies within a plane; that is, it is two-dimensional.

Parallelogram	**Rectangle**	**Square**	**Rhombus**
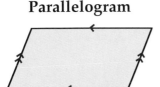	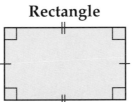	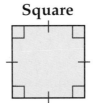	
A *parallelogram* has two pairs of opposite sides that are parallel.	A *rectangle* is a parallelogram with four right angles.	A *square* is a parallelogram with four right angles and four equal sides.	A *rhombus* is a parallelogram with four equal sides.

Look carefully at the figures above, and make sure that you can recognize the symbol that indicates that an angle is a right angle.

A *right angle* measures 90°.

Two right angles added together form a *straight angle* (a line) that measures 180°.

Objects that are exactly the same size and same shape are *congruent*.

┌─ Example ─────────────────────────────────────

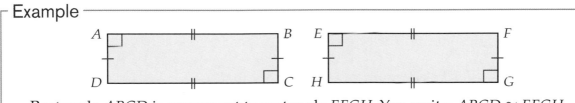

Rectangle *ABCD* is congruent to rectangle *EFGH*. You write: *ABCD* ≅ *EFGH*.

In geometry, you use *congruence marks* (| and ‖) to show that parts of a figure are congruent.

Work Time

1. Explain how you can tell that these two figures are rectangles.

2. Use a 3 × 5-inch index card to represent a rectangle, or use a straightedge to draw a rectangle on grid paper and then cut it out.

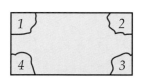

- Label the four corners.

- Tear off the four corners of the rectangle.

- Put the four corners (*vertices*) together, as shown right.

   a. What is the measure of ∠3 + ∠4? Say why.

   b. What is the measure of ∠1 + ∠2? Say why.

   c. What is the measure of ∠1 + ∠3? Say why.

   d. What is the measure of ∠2 + ∠4? Say why.

   e. What is the measure of ∠1 + ∠2 + ∠3 + ∠4? Say why.

3. On a sheet of paper, use a straightedge to draw any large quadrilateral and label the four interior angles *1, 2, 3,* and *4.*

   An *interior angle* is an angle inside a figure.

   - Cut out your quadrilateral, and tear it into four parts so each part contains one of the angles *1, 2, 3,* and *4.*

   - Rearrange the pieces so the four vertices meet at a point.

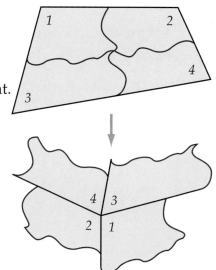

   a. What can you say about the sum of the measures of the four angles around the point?

   b. What does your answer to part a tell you about the sum of the measures of the interior angles of a quadrilateral?

4. Calculate the measure of each unknown angle.

a.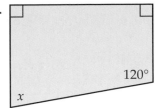

b.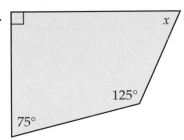

Preparing for the Closing

Think about and answer the following problems. Be prepared to discuss your answers with the class.

5. Can a quadrilateral have four right angles? Why or why not? Give two specific examples.

6. Decide whether each statement is *always true, sometimes true*, or *never true*. Justify your answers using the number properties and the definitions that you know.

a. A right angle measures 90°.

b. The sum of the measures of the angles that form a straight line equals 180°.

CONCEPT BOOK
Review angle types on page 216.

7. An *acute angle* has a measure of less than 90°. Can a quadrilateral have four acute angles? Why or why not? Use figures to support your justification.

8. The sum of the measures of the interior angles of a rectangle is 360°. Write an explanation or show how you know this to be true.

Solve.

a. 42 • 51 =

b. 42 • 56 =

c. 42 • 58 =

d. 42 • 61 =

e. 42 • 65 =

f. 42 • 81 =

g. 4.2 • 51 =

h. 4.2 • 65 =

i. 4.2 • 75 =

> **Hint:** Rewrite each problem as an easier problem that you can calculate in your head.
> For example, 12 • 13 can be written as 10(10 + 3) + 2(10 + 3).

Review and Consolidation

1. What is the sum of the measures of the interior angles in any quadrilateral? Explain.

2. Why can all squares also be called rectangles?

3. What is the measure of ∠1 + ∠3 + ∠4 in the figure at right?

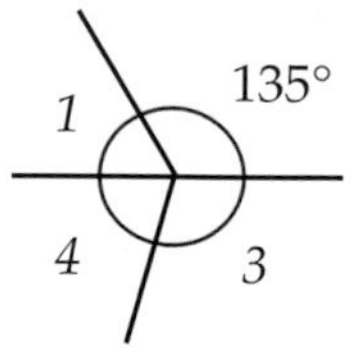

4. Is it possible for a quadrilateral to have four obtuse angles? Why or why not? Sketch figures to help.

Comment

An obtuse angle is larger than 90° but less than 180°.

Homework

1. What is the measure of each interior angle of a rectangle?

2. Use the definition of a rectangle to calculate the sum of the measures of the interior angles of any rectangle.

3. The measures of three angles in a given quadrilateral are 90°, 90°, and 90°.

   a. What is the measure of the unknown angle? Say why.

   b. What type of quadrilateral could this figure be? Say why.

4. What is the measure of ∠x in this figure? Say why.

5. What is the measure of ∠1 + ∠2 + ∠3 + ∠4 in this figure? Explain.

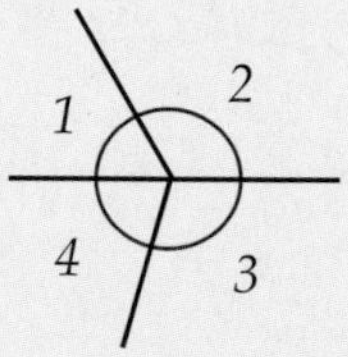

RELATING QUADRILATERALS AND TRIANGLES

GOAL

To learn about the interior angles of rectangles and triangles.

Rosa and Jamal were working on decorations for a school party. They wanted sparkling triangular shapes to hang from the ceiling. First, they had to cut out pairs of triangles of different shapes and sizes.

> **CONCEPT BOOK**
>
> See pages 218–219, 223–224, and 228.

Jamal said, "I know a *triangle* is a closed plane figure with three sides and three angles, but I'm not sure how that will help me make triangles."

Rosa said, "If we start with any quadrilateral, like a rectangle, square, or parallelogram, we can split the quadrilateral into two triangles by cutting along one of the *diagonals*. These are the lines that run across the figure and connect two corners that are not next to each other."

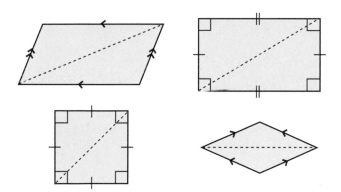

"That makes it easier," said Jamal. "I can cut a rectangular piece of paper into a square, a parallelogram, or a rhombus. Then I can cut that quadrilateral along a diagonal and get two triangles!"

"Okay, we're in business," said Rosa. "As you are cutting, here's something to think about: Are two congruent triangles formed every time a quadrilateral is cut along one of its diagonals?"

Work Time

1. Sketch any quadrilateral on a sheet of paper, and then cut the quadrilateral along one of its diagonals.

   a. Write a description of the resulting shapes.

   b. How many interior angles are in each shape?

2. Now you will explore the sum of the interior angle measures of a triangle from another perspective. Use both triangles made in problem 1. Label the angles in one triangle *A*, *B*, and *C*. Label the angles in the other triangle *D*, *E*, and *F*. Tear each triangle into three parts so that each part contains one of the angles.

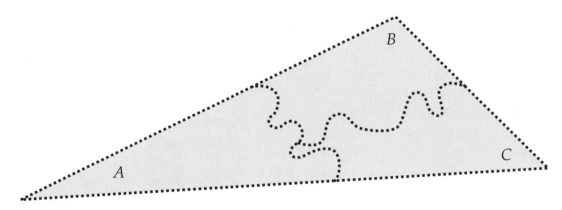

Take the three pieces from the triangle with angles *A*, *B*, and *C* and rearrange them so the three vertices meet at a point.

> **Comment**
>
> Vertices is the plural of vertex.

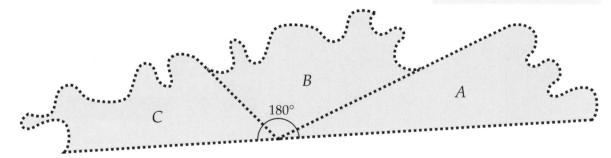

Repeat this exercise with the second triangle from problem 1.

   a. What do you know about the sum of the measures of angles that form a straight line?

   b. What does this say about the sum of the measures of the interior angles of a triangle?

3. Any quadrilateral can be split into two triangles. How do your results from problem 2 part b support what you learned in the last lesson about the sum of the measures of the interior angles of any quadrilateral? Use figures to help explain your answer.

4. Cut along the diagonal of a sheet of paper to create two large congruent triangles.

    a. Measure the angles with a protractor. Check your measurements to make sure that the sum of the measures of the three interior angles is 180°.

    b. Place congruent sides of the two triangles together to form a quadrilateral. Sketch the figure you get, and, without measuring, calculate the measures of the four angles in your quadrilateral.

    c. Repeat part b in different ways, either by turning over one of the triangles or by putting together a different pair of congruent sides.

    d. Compare your results with those of your partner.

    e. Did you both obtain some shapes that were parallelograms?

    f. For each quadrilateral that you made, check that the sum of the measures of the four interior angles is 360°.

    g. What else is the same about the quadrilaterals that you and your partner made? What is different?

Preparing for the Closing

5. What does *congruent* mean?

6. What is the sum of the measures of the three angles in a triangle?

7. A triangle cannot have more than one right angle. Say why.

8. A triangle can have more than one acute angle. Say why.

Skills

Choose the number that is closest to the correct answer.

a. 101 • 11

Ⓐ 10   Ⓑ 100   Ⓒ 1000   Ⓓ 10,000

b. 254 • 254

Ⓐ 10   Ⓑ 100   Ⓒ 1000   Ⓓ 10,000   Ⓔ 100,000   Ⓕ 1,000,000

c. 111 • 999

Ⓐ 10   Ⓑ 100   Ⓒ 1000   Ⓓ 10,000   Ⓔ 100,000   Ⓕ 1,000,000

d. 80 • 19 • 16

Ⓐ 10   Ⓑ 100   Ⓒ 1000   Ⓓ 10,000   Ⓔ 100,000   Ⓕ 1,000,000

e. 30 • 41 • 82

Ⓐ 10   Ⓑ 100   Ⓒ 1000   Ⓓ 10,000   Ⓔ 100,000   Ⓕ 1,000,000

Review and Consolidation

1. Try to sketch a triangle with two obtuse angles. Say why you think this is not possible.

2. Calculate the measure of the unknown angle(s) in each triangle.

> **Comment**
>
> The sum of the measures of the interior angles of any triangle is 180°.

a.

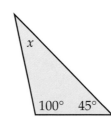

b.

3. Discuss with a partner how you found the answers to problem 2.

Homework

1. Calculate the measure of the unknown angle in each triangle.

a.

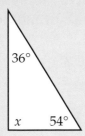

b.

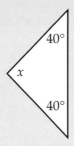

c.

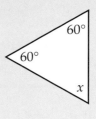

2. Justify your answers using what you know about the sum of the measures of the angles of any triangle. Sketch figures to support your answer.

  a. Is it possible for a triangle to have no obtuse angles?

  b. Is it possible for a triangle to have two right angles?

  c. Is it possible for a triangle to have no right angles?

  d. Is it possible for a triangle to have both a right angle and an obtuse angle?

To identify different types of triangles, and to classify them using their characteristics.

A *polygon* is a plane figure. *Poly-* means many; *-gon* means angles.

You know that triangles are three-sided polygons. Triangles have the smallest number of sides and angles possible for a polygon. The sum of the measures of the three angles in any triangle is 180°.

<table>
<tr><td>CONCEPT BOOK</td></tr>
<tr><td>See pages 215–216, 218, and 220.</td></tr>
</table>

Triangles can be classified by the sizes of their angles.

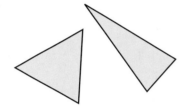
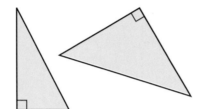
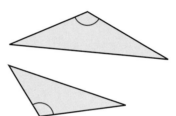

Acute triangles have three acute angles.	*Right triangles* have one right angle.	*Obtuse triangles* have one obtuse angle.
An *acute angle* measures less than 90°.	A *right angle* measures exactly 90°.	An *obtuse angle* is greater than 90° but less than 180°.

Triangles can also be classified according to the lengths of their sides.

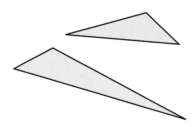
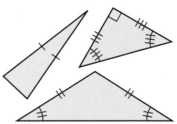
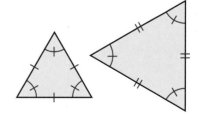

In *scalene triangles* all three sides have different lengths.	In *isosceles triangles* two sides have the same length.	In *equilateral triangles* all three sides have the same length.

As you learned in Lesson 6, congruence marks are used to show that parts of a figure are congruent. In isosceles and equilateral triangles, the congruent sides have congruent angles opposite them. Note that when there are no congruence marks, as in the scalene triangles, none of the sides or angles are equal.

Work Time

1. Using Handout 1: *Types of Triangles* and a straightedge or ruler, sketch an example of each triangle described below.

   The descriptions of the triangles are based on:

   - The sizes of their angles
   - The lengths of their sides

   Mark angles and sides with congruence marks when appropriate.

   a. Acute Triangle:
   All angles measure less than 90°.

   b. Equilateral Triangle:
   All three sides have the same length.

   c. Scalene Triangle:
   All three sides have different lengths.

   d. Obtuse Triangle:
   One angle measures more than 90° and less than 180°.

   e. Right Triangle:
   One angle measures exactly 90°.

   f. Isosceles Triangle:
   Two sides are the same length.

Lesson 8	Types of Triangles
Handout **1**	

a. Acute Triangle	b. Equilateral Triangle
c. Scalene Triangle	d. Obtuse Triangle
e. Right Triangle	f. Isosceles Triangle

Preparing for the Closing

2. Decide whether the following statements are *always true, sometimes true,* or *never true.* Justify your answers.

   a. If a triangle is isosceles, then it has at least two congruent sides.

   b. If a triangle is equilateral, then it has three congruent sides.

   c. If a triangle is equilateral, it can also be a right triangle.

3. An equilateral triangle is a special kind of isosceles triangle. Say why.

4. The largest angle in an equilateral triangle has a measure of 60°. Say why.

Skills

Copy and complete this table.

Number	× 10	× 100	× 1000
19.5			
0.326			
1.745			
5.007			
5.16			

Review and Consolidation

1. a. Lisa and Jamal drew the triangles below, but labeled only the right angles. Now, they want to classify the triangles into three different groups *based on the sizes of their angles.*

Help them sort the triangles in groups of acute triangles, obtuse triangles, and right triangles.

Comment

Classify means to arrange into groups that have common features.

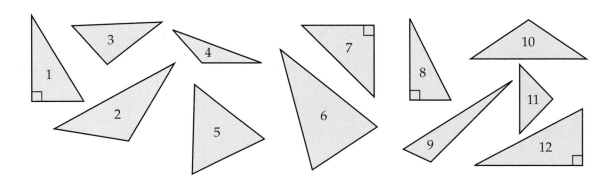

b. Write the definitions for each of the three different groups of triangles in part a.

2. a. Sort the following triangles into three different groups *based on the lengths of their sides.*

Use the congruence marks as your guide—do not make guesses based on appearances. Some triangles may fit into more than one group.

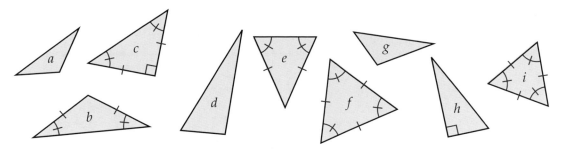

b. Write a definition for each of the three groups of triangles in part a.

3. What can you say about the angles of an isosceles triangle?

4. Sketch an isosceles right triangle. Label the right angle, and use congruence marks to show equal side lengths.

Homework

1. Sketch each triangle described below. Show all angles and marks of congruence. If you cannot sketch the triangle, say why.

a. Isosceles triangle with one right angle

b. Equilateral triangle

c. Triangle with two obtuse angles

d. Triangle with two right angles

e. Scalene triangle with one right angle

f. Triangle with three congruent sides

2. Which two parts of problem 1 describe the same triangle?

LESSON

9 CALCULATING THE MEASURE OF AN ANGLE

GOAL

To label angles, and to use the sum of the measures of the interior angles of a triangle to calculate the measure of one unknown angle.

An angle can be labeled with a single letter.

The three angles shown here are angle A, angle B, and angle C.

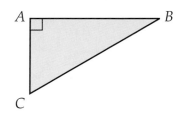

CONCEPT BOOK

See pages 212–213, 219, and 221–222.

You can also refer to an angle by using these conventions:

$\angle$ means that you are referring to an angle (rather than a side or a point).

$\angle ABC$ means that you are referring to an angle formed by the line from point A to point B meeting the line from point B to point C.

The middle letter is always the vertex of the angle.
The *vertex* is the point where the sides of the angle come together.
B is the vertex of $\angle ABC$.

Example

In this figure:

The angle with measure 30° is $\angle DFE$ or $\angle EFD$ or $\angle F$.

The right angle is $\angle DEF$ or $\angle FED$ or $\angle E$.

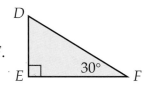

You will use these conventions for labeling triangles as you investigate how to calculate the measure of the unknown angle $\angle EDF$.

Example

Let x stand for the measure of the unknown angle, D.

You know that the sum of the three angle measures is 180°, so:

$x + 30° + 90° = 180°$

Solving this equation gives $x = 60°$.

The measure of $\angle EDF = 60°$.

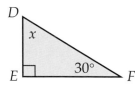

Work Time

1. Sometimes, you estimate the measure of angles by looking at them. In this problem, you are not going to estimate the measures of the unknown angles. Instead, it is your job to calculate the measure of each unknown angle. Do not try to estimate, because none of the figures are drawn to scale.

Calculate the measure of each angle indicated, and explain how you found the measure. Use what you know about the sum of the measures of the angles in a triangle. Remember, the middle letter is always the vertex of the angle.

a. Calculate the measure of ∠ACB.

How do you know?

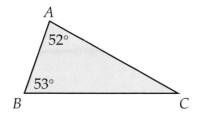

b. Calculate the measure of ∠ACB.

How do you know?

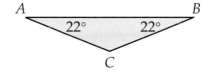

c. Calculate the measure of ∠MNO.

How do you know?

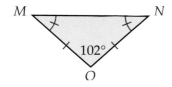

d. Calculate the measure of ∠BAC.

How do you know?

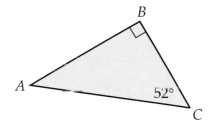

e. ∠DBC is a straight angle.
Calculate the measure of ∠ABD.

How do you know?

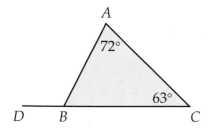

f. ∠DAB is a straight angle.
Calculate the measure of ∠DAC.

How do you know?

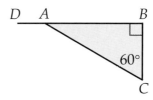

g. *A*, *B*, and *D* lie on a line.
   Calculate the measure of ∠*BDC*.

   How do you know?

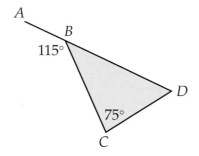

h. *B*, *C*, and *D* lie on a line.
   Calculate the measure of ∠*BCA*.

   How do you know?

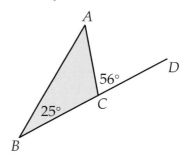

2. a. Calculate the measure of each missing angle in the
   figure at right.

   Label the angles in your answers.

   b. Explain how you know the measure of each angle.

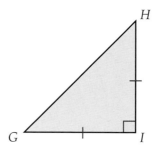

Preparing for the Closing

3. a. Label the unknown angle in this triangle.

   b. What is the vertex of this angle?

   c. What is the measure of this angle?

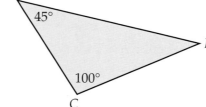

4. In the figures for problem 1, parts e–h,
   an angle, called an *exterior angle*, is formed
   by extending one of the sides of the triangle beyond the vertex.

   How is the measure of the
   exterior angle related to
   the measure of its adjacent
   interior angle?

   Hint: ∠*BCD* is an exterior angle.
   ∠*BCA* is the interior angle that is
   adjacent to ∠*BCD*.

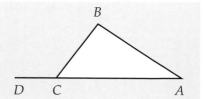

   Explain.

5. Do the lengths of the lines that form an angle determine the measure of that angle?
   Explain your thinking.

Skills

Calculate.

a. $763 + 57 =$ b. $286 + 39 =$ c. $802 + 99 =$ d. $178 + 195 =$

e. $361 + 279 =$ f. $1028 + 234 =$ g. $4190 + 649 =$ h. $2409 + 1235 =$

> **Hint:** Rewrite each problem as an easier problem that you can calculate in your head. For example, $537 + 218$ can be written as $(500 + 200) + (30 + 10) + (7 + 8)$.

Review and Consolidation

1. This figure shows three exterior angles: $\angle DAE$, $\angle EBF$, and $\angle FCD$.

Each one forms a line and shares a common vertex and side with its corresponding interior angle.

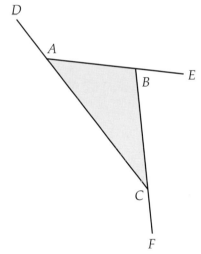

a. Write the names of two angles that both have A as their common vertex.

b. Explain why the sum of the measures of these two angles is $180°$.

c. Explain why the sum of the measures of all six angles in the figure is $540°$.

d. Using what you learned in part c, explain why the sum of the measures of the three exterior angles is $360°$.

> **Hint:** Use the sum of the measures of the interior angles of a triangle.

2. Calculate the measures of the unknown angles in each figure.

> **Hint:** You should have a total of three interior angle measures and three exterior angle measures for each triangle.

a.

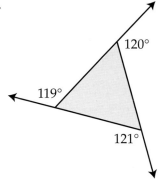

b.

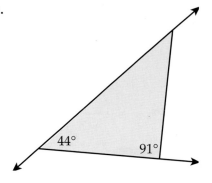

c.

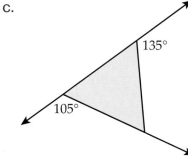

d.

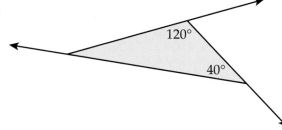

e.

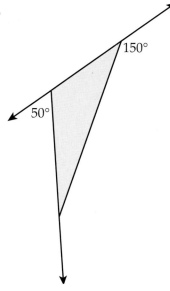

f.

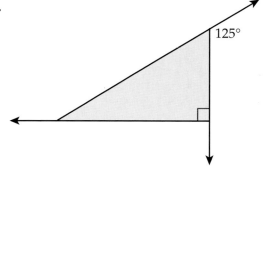

Homework

1. Calculate the measures of the angles indicated. Show all of your work.

a. ∠GHI

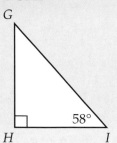

b. ∠HGI

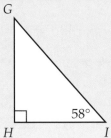

c. ∠DEF

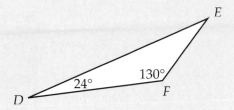

d. ∠JKL, ∠KLJ, ∠LJK

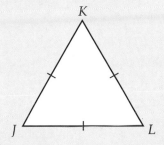

e. ∠OMN, ∠MNO

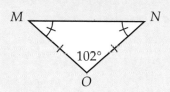

f. ∠TUV, ∠UVT, ∠VTU

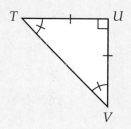

g. ∠PRQ, ∠RPQ

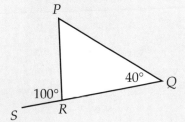

h. ∠RPQ

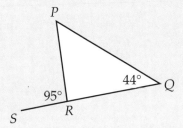

To review what you have learned about quadrilaterals and triangles.

Chen made this poster to show all that he knows about triangles. Use it to help you answer the problems in Work Time.

CONCEPT BOOK

See pages 212–229.

Putting It Together

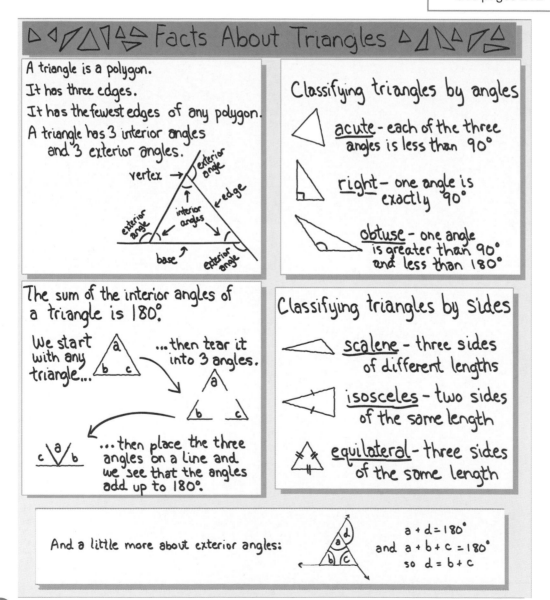

Work Time

1. In which triangle, *A* or *B*, is the sum of the measures of the interior angles greater?

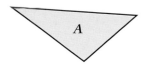 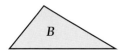

2. Sketch examples of the following triangles. Show congruence marks where necessary.

　a. An isosceles right triangle

　b. An acute triangle

　c. An equilateral triangle

3. A line forms a straight angle. What is the measure of a straight angle?

4. Calculate the measures of the unknown angles indicated.
Justify your answers.

　a. ∠*ABC* and ∠*ACD*

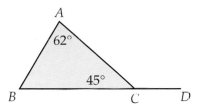

　b. ∠*DEF* and ∠*CDE*

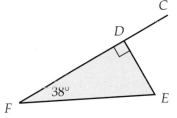

　c. ∠*ABC* and ∠*ADC*

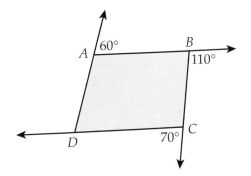

　d. ∠*ADE* and ∠*BCF*

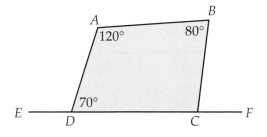

Comment

Not all the figures are drawn to scale.

Putting It Together

5. Name each of the three unknown angles in the figure at right, and calculate their measures.

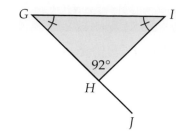

6. a. A triangle has one interior angle measuring 30°, and another interior angle measuring 50°. What is the measure of the third interior angle?

   b. Make a sketch of this triangle.

   c. What type of triangle is it?

7. a. A triangle has one exterior angle measuring 50°, and another exterior angle measuring 160°. What are the measures of each of the interior angles of this triangle?

   b. Make a sketch of this triangle.

   c. What type of triangle is it?

Preparing for the Closing

8. What is the measure of each interior angle of an equilateral triangle? Explain how you know.

9. What is the sum of the measures of the interior angles of an equilateral triangle? Explain how you know.

10. What is the measure of each exterior angle of an equilateral triangle? Explain how you know.

Skills

Solve.

   a. What number is 0.01 more than 5.99?

   b. What number is 0.01 more than 0.45?

   c. What number is 0.1 more than 6.9?

   d. What number is 0.01 more than 6.9?

   e. What number must be added to 756 to give an answer of 1000?

   f. What number must be added to 0.678 to give an answer of 1?

Putting It Together

Review and Consolidation

Work with a partner to make a "Facts about Quadrilaterals" poster similar to the one about triangles on the first page of this lesson. Include a section about the different types of quadrilaterals and a section on the measures of the angles of quadrilaterals.

Follow these four steps to create your poster. Read all the steps before you start.

1. Discuss with your partner what should be included on the poster and how it should be presented.

2. Make a rough draft of the poster.

3. Present the draft to the class and get feedback about two aspects of your work:

   Content

   - Does the poster include all the important information on the topic?

   - Does the poster include examples to illustrate the important information?

   Presentation

   - Does the poster present the information in a way that is organized and that results in a useful reference for future work?

   - Is the poster easy to read?

4. Use the feedback to make a final draft of the poster.

Homework

1. Name each of the angles in this figure, and calculate the measure of each interior angle.

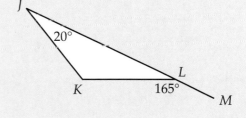

2. Sketch the triangles described below, and then calculate the measure of the third interior angle.

   a. One interior angle is 60° and another interior angle is 60°.

   b. One interior angle is 45° and another interior angle is 45°.

   c. One interior angle is 60° and another interior angle is 30°.

   d. One interior angle is 110° and another interior angle is 35°.

   e. One interior angle is 86° and another interior angle is 47°.

   f. One exterior angle is 120° and another exterior angle is 117°.

3. Classify each triangle in problem 2 based on its angles.

Putting It Together

GOAL

To learn more about polygons, and to calculate the measures of their interior and exterior angles.

Polygons

Polygons are two-dimensional, closed figures with three or more sides that are line segments. The sides meet at vertices and do not cross each other.

CONCEPT BOOK

See pages 217, 221, 223–226, and 228–229.

All polygons are either regular or irregular.

Regular polygons have sides of equal measure and interior angles of equal measure.

Irregular polygons have sides of unequal measure and interior angles of unequal measure.

Example

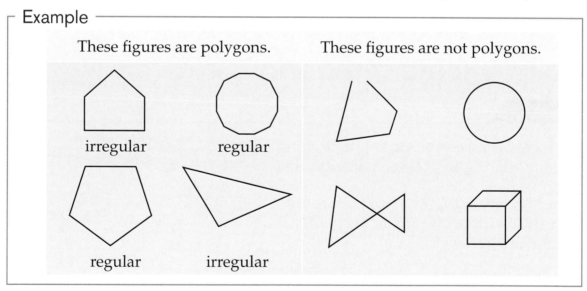

These figures are polygons.

irregular   regular

regular   irregular

These figures are not polygons.

Interior Angles

The size and number of the interior angles help define a polygon.

A *triangle* is a polygon that has three sides and three interior angles.

A *quadrilateral* is a polygon that has four sides and four interior angles.

A pentagon is another type of polygon. *Penta-* means five, so a *pentagon* has five sides and five interior angles.

Exterior Angles of a Polygon

An *exterior angle* is formed when a side of a polygon is extended beyond the vertex.

Any two angles with one arm in common are called *adjacent angles*. An exterior angle, e, and its adjacent interior angle, i, always form a straight angle ($e + i = 180°$).

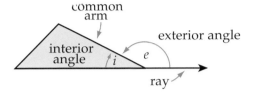

Angles at a Point

Suppose you have a circular arrangement of angles, and you expand the center point to form a figure, as shown below. The angles now form the exterior angles of a polygon.

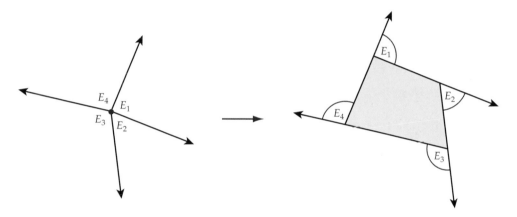

The sum of the exterior angle measures of a polygon is 360°.

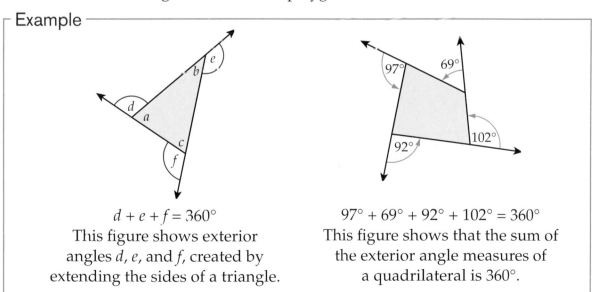

Example

$d + e + f = 360°$
This figure shows exterior angles d, e, and f, created by extending the sides of a triangle.

$97° + 69° + 92° + 102° = 360°$
This figure shows that the sum of the exterior angle measures of a quadrilateral is 360°.

1. In each figure, calculate the unknown measures for the interior angles and exterior angles.

a.

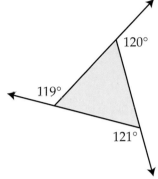

b.

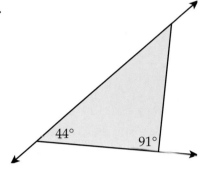

2. a. Sketch a pentagon. Label the five exterior angles.

   b. The sum of the exterior angle measures of a pentagon is 360°.

   What is the sum of the interior angle measures?

3. A polygon has a set of exterior angles labeled, and then all of its sides are shrunk down to length zero. This figure shows all that remains.

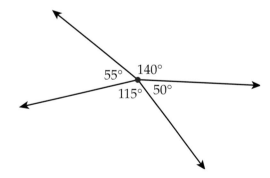

   a. How many sides did the figure have originally, and what were the measures of its interior angles?

   b. Explain how the concepts in this problem can be used to prove that the sum of the measures of the exterior angles of a quadrilateral is 360°.

4. There is something wrong with each of these figures. Explain the errors.

a.

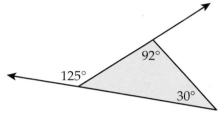

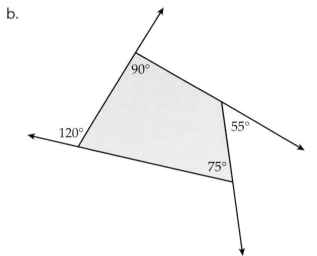

b.

Hint: An exterior angle and its adjacent interior angle always form a straight angle (180°).

Preparing for the Closing

5. In this quadrilateral, $e + f + g + h = 360°$.

Show why $a + b + c + d = 360°$.

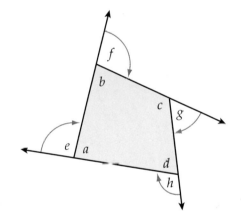

6. It is true that a quadrilateral can be cut into two triangles by sketching a diagonal.

It is also true that the sum of the interior angle measures of a triangle is 180°.

Use these two facts to verify the fact that the sum of the interior angle measures of a quadrilateral is 360°. Sketch a figure to support your answer.

7. In the triangle at right:

a. $a + b + c = 180°$. Say why.

b. $d = b + c$. Say why.

c. What does this problem tell you about the relationship between the exterior angle of a triangle and its two opposite interior angles?

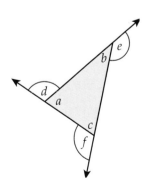

Skills

Calculate.

a. $4821 - 514 =$ 　　　　b. $6743 - 461 =$ 　　　　c. $9674 - 853 =$

d. $5645 - 1317 =$ 　　　　e. $8769 - 3292 =$ 　　　　f. $7356 - 4731 =$

g. $7613 - 185 =$ 　　　　h. $6094 - 428 =$ 　　　　i. $694 - 428 =$

Review and Consolidation

1. Find the measure of each unknown angle in quadrilateral *ABCD*.

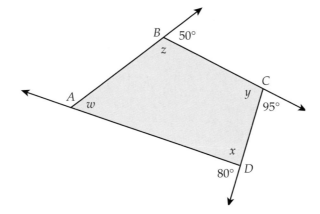

2. Write two methods for calculating the measure of the exterior angle at *A*.

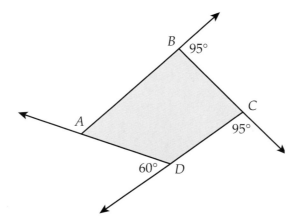

3. Explain how the unknown exterior angle in each of the following figures can be calculated without first calculating interior angle *A*.

a.

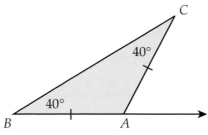

b.

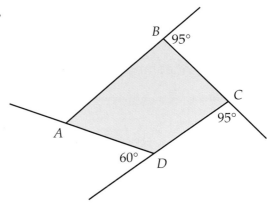

Homework

1. In these triangles, calculate the measure of each unknown interior angle.

a.

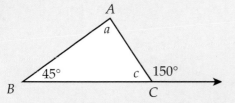

b.

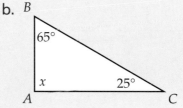

2. Calculate the measure of *x* in each figure. Explain your reasoning.

a.

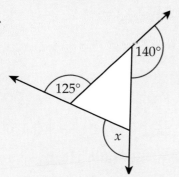

b.

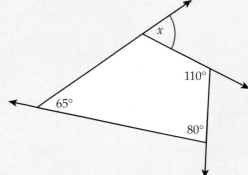

3. Sketch a hexagon. Label the figure and mark the six exterior angles. The sum of the exterior angle measures is 360°. What is the sum of the interior angle measures of this polygon?

> **Hint:** *Hexa-* is a prefix that means six.

LESSON

12 THE PYTHAGOREAN THEOREM

GOAL

To use the Pythagorean theorem for right triangles.

In a right triangle, the side opposite the right angle is called the *hypotenuse*. The two shorter sides of the right triangle are sometimes called the *legs*.

CONCEPT BOOK

See pages 247–249.

Example

Each of these triangles is a right triangle because it has one right angle. In each, the right angle is at vertex B.

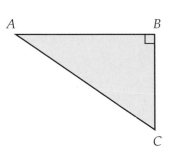

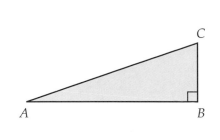

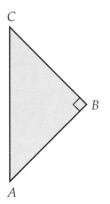

In each of these triangles, the hypotenuse is segment AC and the legs are segments AB and BC.

In this right triangle, the two shorter sides measure 9 units and 12 units. The measure of the hypotenuse is 15 units.

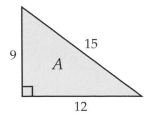

In this figure, a square has been constructed on each side of the right triangle.

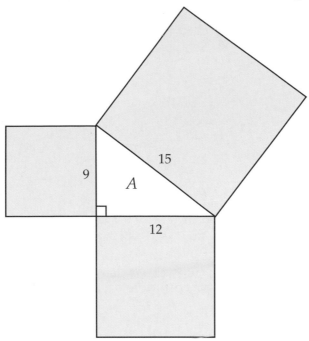

The square on the shortest side has an area of $9 \bullet 9 = 9^2 = 81$ square units.
The square on the second shortest side has an area of $12 \bullet 12 = 12^2 = 144$ square units.
The square on the hypotenuse has an area of $15 \bullet 15 = 15^2 = 225$ square units.

If you add $81 + 144$, you get 225—the same as the area of the square of the hypotenuse.

Pythagoras (a mathematician in ancient Greece) discovered that *in all right triangles,* when you add the squares of the two shorter sides, you get a value equal to the square of the hypotenuse.

This property is called the *Pythagorean theorem.*

> In any right triangle, the square of the measure of the hypotenuse is equal to the sum of the squares of the measures of the two shorter sides.

If you use the letters a and b to stand for the measures of the two shorter sides, and the letter c to stand for the measure of the hypotenuse, then the theorem can be represented by the formula $c^2 = a^2 + b^2$.

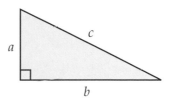

You can use this theorem to calculate the length of unknown sides in right triangles.

Work Time

1. Triangle 1 is a right triangle, but triangles 2 and 3 are not. Say why.

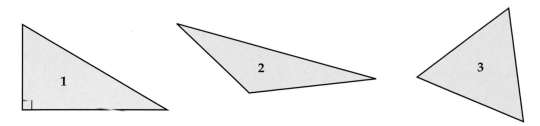

2. Verify that the Pythagorean theorem works for each of the right triangles *B* through *E* on the next page. (The calculation for triangle *A* from the lesson introduction has already been done for you.)

   To show the calculations, copy and complete a table like this one.

Triangle	Sum of the Squares of the Two Legs	Square of the Hypotenuse
A	$9^2 + 12^2 = 81 + 144 = 225$	$15^2 = 225$
B		
C		
D		
E		

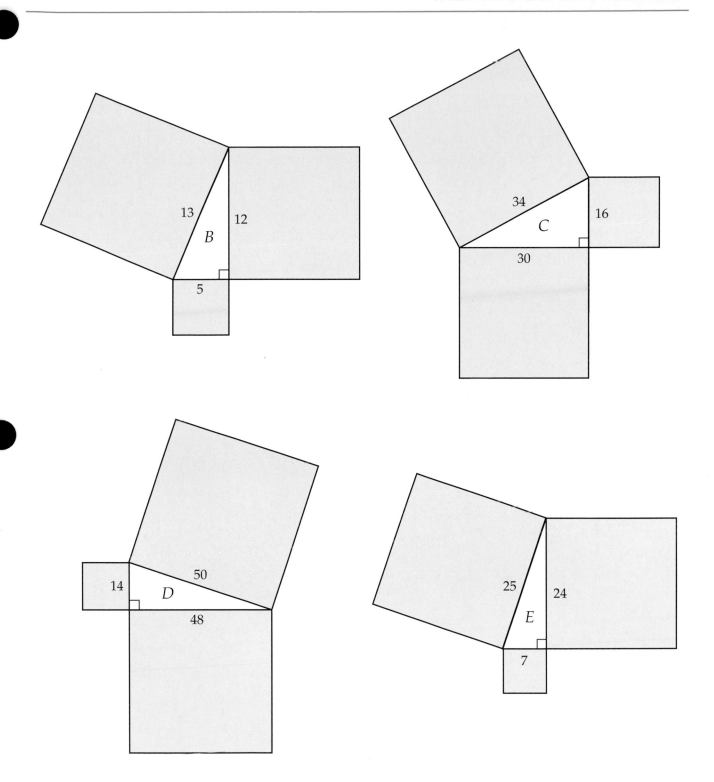

3. Verify whether these sets of numbers represent the side lengths of right triangles.

> **Hint:** To do this, you need to calculate the squares to see if they satisfy the Pythagorean theorem.

    a. { 3, 5, 7 }   b. { 5, 12, 13 }   c. { 7, 9, 11 }   d. { 6, 8, 10 }

4. You should have found that the Pythagorean theorem works for two of the sets of numbers in problem 3. Sketch and label these two right triangles. Label the sides with their measures.

5. Use the Pythagorean theorem to calculate the length of the hypotenuse in each of the right triangles below. Where necessary, round your answer to one decimal place. (The first calculation has been completed as an example.)

	Right Triangle	$a^2 + b^2$	c^2	Hypotenuse
a.	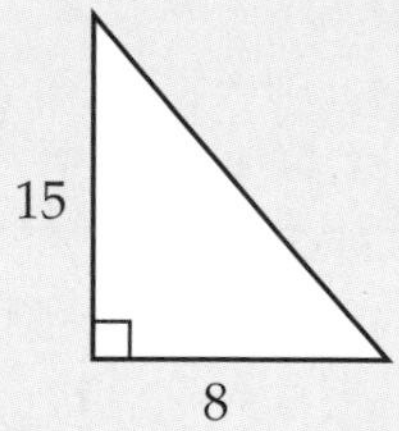	$8^2 + 15^2 = 289$	289	$c = \sqrt{289} = 17$
b.	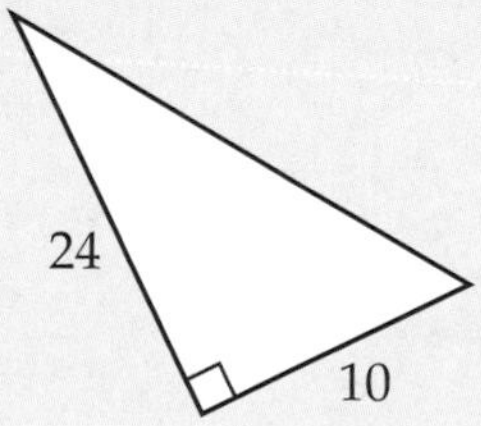			
c.	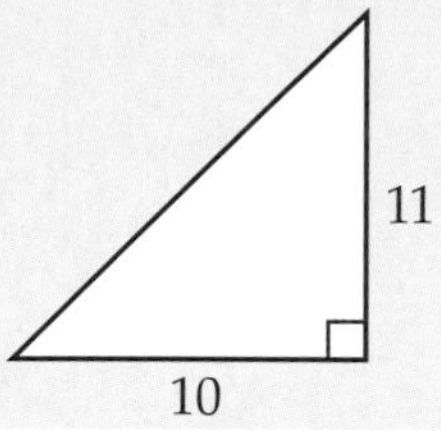			
d.	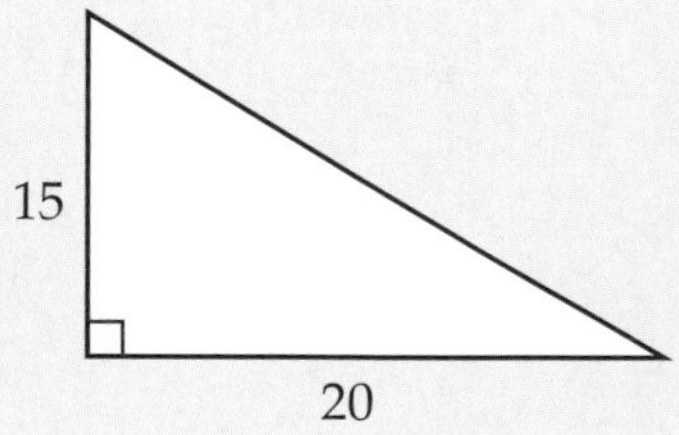			
e.	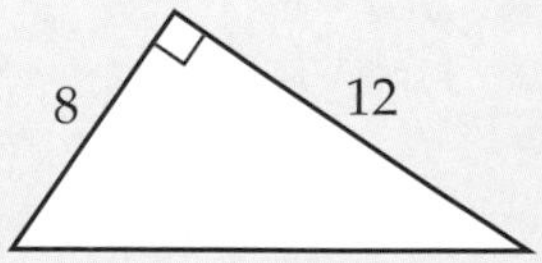			

Preparing for the Closing

6. Write in words how you can find the length of the hypotenuse of a right triangle if you know the lengths of the two legs.

7. Lisa and Jamal were given this problem to solve.

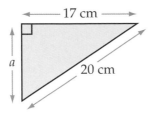

Jamal said that the problem is impossible to solve because the Pythagorean theorem is used for finding the hypotenuse.

Lisa said she thought the formula could be used somehow, but she could not quite figure out how.

Can you help? Discuss this problem with your partner and write your method in your notebook.

8. You have learned that the relationship $c^2 = a^2 + b^2$ (where c is the longest side) always holds true for right triangles.

In obtuse triangles, $c^2 > a^2 + b^2$. In acute triangles, $c^2 < a^2 + b^2$.

a. Which set of numbers in problem 3 represents the side measures of an obtuse triangle?

b. Which set represents an acute triangle?

Skills

Solve.

a. $25.50 + $0.40 =	b. $25.50 + $0.50 =	c. $25.50 + $0.60 =
d. $25.50 + $1.40 =	e. $25.50 + $1.50 =	f. $25.50 + $1.60 =
g. $25.50 + $40 =	h. $25.50 + $50 =	i. $25.50 + $5.50 =

Review and Consolidation

1. Your teacher will give a copy of Handout 2: *Card Sort*, which has a set of fifteen cards.

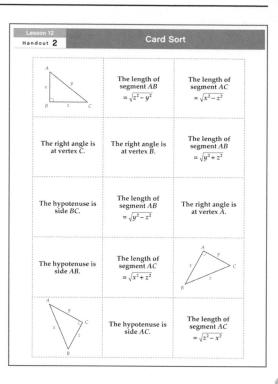

a. Your first task is to sort the cards into three sets of five cards. Each set will have:

- A figure of a right triangle

- A statement about the right angle

- A statement about the hypotenuse

- A calculation to determine the length of $\overline{AC}$

- A calculation to determine the length of $\overline{AB}$

b. After you have completed the card sort, prepare an explanation of your work to present to another student or the whole class.

Homework

1. Here are the squares of some numbers.

$$45^2 = 2025 \qquad 19^2 = 361 \qquad 26^2 = 676 \qquad 18^2 = 324 \qquad 27^2 = 729$$

Use them to find the square roots of these numbers.

a. $\sqrt{361} =$ b. $\sqrt{676} =$ c. $\sqrt{729} =$ d. $\sqrt{2025} =$ e. $\sqrt{324} =$

2. Use a calculator to help you check whether the sets of integers below satisfy the Pythagorean theorem. For any that do, sketch and label a corresponding right triangle.

a. $\{2, 3, 4\}$ b. $\{15, 20, 25\}$ c. $\{10, 24, 26\}$ d. $\{5, 10, 15\}$

3. Find the length of the hypotenuse of each right triangle. Where necessary, round the answer to one decimal place.

a.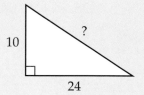

b.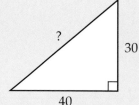

c.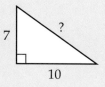

d.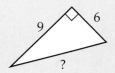

ESTIMATING SQUARE ROOTS

GOAL

To use the "trial and improvement" strategy to estimate square roots.

A *square root* is one of two equal factors that have a certain product.

CONCEPT BOOK

See pages 339–341.

Example

Five is the square root of 25 because 5 multiplied by itself equals 25.

$$5 \bullet 5 = 25 \qquad \sqrt{25} = 5$$

Note: The symbol $\sqrt{}$ stands for "the positive square root of." For example, $\sqrt{25}$ means +5.

Squares and square roots are inverses—just as multiplication and division are inverses.

Some square roots are rational numbers and some are not rational.

Example

Five is a rational number, so $\sqrt{25}$ is rational.

$\sqrt{3}$ and $\sqrt{7}$ are *irrational*. This means that they cannot be written as terminating or repeating decimals.

Here is the formula for calculating the area of a square:

Area equals the length of a side squared, $A = x^2$, where x is the length of a side.

x

$A = x^2$ x

$x^2 = x \bullet x \qquad x$ squared equals x multiplied by x. So, $5^2 = 5 \bullet 5 = 25$.

Example

If the area of a square is 2 cm², what is the length of a side?

Each side must be $\sqrt{2}$ cm.

You know this by asking, "What number multiplied by itself equals 2?"

Based on the definition of square root, it must be the square root of 2.

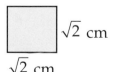

$\sqrt{2}$ cm

$\sqrt{2}$ cm

$A = 2$ cm²

You can estimate an irrational square root by finding a terminating decimal that is close to the square root. An *estimate* is approximately equal to the square root; it is not exactly equal to the square root.

> **Example**
>
> To find $\sqrt{2}$, try numbers until you get very close to a product of 2.
>
> | | |
> |---|---|
> | $1 \cdot 1 = 1$ | too small |
> | $2 \cdot 2 = 4$ | too large |
> | $1.5 \cdot 1.5 = 2.25$ | too large |
> | $1.4 \cdot 1.4 = 1.96$ | too small |
> | $1.41 \cdot 1.41 = 1.9881$ | too small |
> | $1.42 \cdot 1.42 = 2.0164$ | too large |
>
> What value of x would you try next?

Work Time

1. The example above estimates the value of $\sqrt{2}$.

   Calculate a better estimate to three decimal places using 1.415 and 1.414 as values for x.

   a. Multiply $1.415 \cdot 1.415$.

   b. How much greater is $(1.415 \cdot 1.415)$ than 2?

   c. Multiply $1.414 \cdot 1.414$.

   d. How much less is $(1.414 \cdot 1.414)$ than 2?

   e. What is the best estimate of $\sqrt{2}$ to three decimal places?

2. a. Copy this table and find the square roots of these numbers.

x	1	4	9	16	25	36	49	64	81	100
$\sqrt{x}$										

   b. Using the answers from from part a and the trial and improvement strategy, estimate the square roots of these numbers.

x	5	7	8	14	26
$\sqrt{x}$					

3. Write the square of each of these numbers.

   a. 0.5   b. 0.8   c. 0.07   d. 1.4

4. Write the square root of each of these numbers.

   a. 0.64   b. 0.25   c. 0.0049   d. 1.96

5. a. The equation $x^2 = 36$ is read as "x squared equals 36." Solve the equation by finding a value of x that makes the equation true.

   b. $x^2 = 25$. Solve for x.

   c. $x^2 = 30$. The solution to $x^2 = 30$ must be between two whole numbers. Which whole numbers are they?   **Hint:** See problem 2a.

   d. Find $\sqrt{30}$ to two decimal places. Use the strategy of trial and improvement, and show your work in a table similar to the example in the Opening.

Preparing for the Closing

6. a. Say why the number 1.41 is a good estimate for the value of $\sqrt{2}$.

   b. Say why the number 1.414 is a better estimate for the value of $\sqrt{2}$ than 1.41.

7. Look again at problems 2, 3, and 4.

   a. Is the square of a number always greater than the number? Say why, using examples.

   b. Is the square root of a number always less than the number? Say why, using examples.

8. Look again at problem 5.

   a. In part a, is the solution of $x^2 = 36$ a whole number? A rational number? Give reasons and examples.

> **CONCEPT BOOK**
>
> See pages 155–157 to review rational and irrational numbers.

   b. In part b, is the solution of $x^2 = 25$ a whole number? A rational number? Give reasons and examples.

   c. In parts c and d, is the solution of $x^2 = 30$ a whole number? A rational number? Give reasons and examples.   **Hint:** See problem 2a.

9. Rosa claimed that x^2 and $2x$ are the same. She justified her claim with the example $2^2 = 4$ and $2 \bullet 2 = 4$.

Do you agree with her? Say why or why not. Does her example justify her claim? Say why or why not.

Skills

Solve.

    a. $382.60 − $0.50 =   b. $382.60 − $0.60 =   c. $382.60 − $0.70 =

    d. $382.60 − $2.50 =   e. $382.60 − $2.60 =   f. $382.60 − $2.70 =

    g. $382.60 + $3.50 =   h. $382.60 + $3.70 =   i. $382.60 + $3.40 =

Review and Consolidation

1. Calculate a value for x that makes each equation true.

    a. $x^2 = 9$ b. $x^2 = 64$ c. $x^2 = 0.81$ d. $x^2 = 0.0025$

2. This square has an area of 45 m² and a side length of x.

    a. The side length is between which two whole numbers?

        Hint: See Work Time problem 2a.

    b. Estimate the side length to two decimal places.

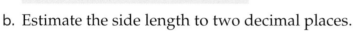

3. This square has an area of 72 m² and a side length of x.

    a. The side length is between which two whole numbers?

        Hint: See Work Time problem 2a.

    b. Estimate the side length to two decimal places.

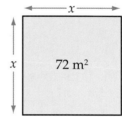

4. Ms. Reynolds challenged her students
dimensions of a cube.

Dwayne remembered that the formula for
the volume of a cube is $V = x^3$ or $V = x \bullet x \bullet x$.

Find the side length of this cube.

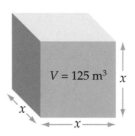

Homework

1. Suppose $x^2 = 8$. You can say that "x squared equals 8," or "x is the *square root* of 8."

    a. Between which two consecutive whole numbers is x?

    b. Which of the two numbers in part a is closer to x?

    c. Estimate x to two decimal places.

    Hint: See Work Time
problem 2a.

PUTTING THE PYTHAGOREAN THEOREM TO WORK

GOAL

To use the Pythagorean theorem to solve problems.

Work Time

Lisa, Dwayne, and Rosa were each given a different problem to solve in math class. Unfortunately, they all made some mistakes in their solutions. You need to figure out *where* each student went wrong and explain *why* the student is wrong. Then complete each problem correctly.

1. A boy scout wants to row from one side of the river to his campsite directly opposite. The width of the river is 30.5 meters.

   However, there is a strong current flowing in the river, so the scout actually rows along the route shown in the diagram. He reaches the other side of the river at a point 52 m away from his campsite.

   How far did the boy scout row? (Express your answer correct to the nearest meter.)

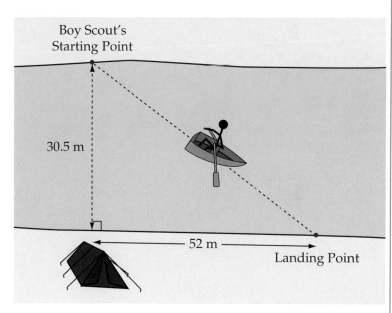

Boy Scout's Starting Point

30.5 m

52 m

Landing Point

   Here is Lisa's solution:

   > The boy scout rowed = 30.5 + 52 = 82.5 m

   a. What mistake did Lisa make?

   b. What is the correct answer? Show your work.

CONCEPT BOOK

See pages 247–249.

Putting Mathematics to Work

2. Mrs. Valdez wants to build a wire fence around the outside of her rectangular field. The diagonal of the field measures 45 yards; the width of the field measures 66 feet.

What amount of wire fencing (to the nearest foot) does Mrs. Valdez need to buy?

Here is Dwayne's solution:

> First you need to calculate the length of the field.
>
> $$\text{length} = \sqrt{\text{diagonal} + \text{width}}$$
> $$= \sqrt{66 + 45} = \sqrt{111} = 10.53 \text{ or about 10 feet}$$
>
> Then you need to add all four of the side measures.
>
> $$\text{Total amount needed} = 10 + 10 + 66 + 66 = 152 \text{ feet}$$

a. What mistake did Dwayne make?

b. What is the correct answer? Show your work.

3. Farmer Brown has a grain bin in the shape of a cone on top of a cylinder.

Calculate the perpendicular height, h, of the bin if the radius of the cylinder is 12 feet, the slant height of the cone is 8 feet, and the height of the cylinder is 1.25 times the height of the cone.

Here is Rosa's solution:

> $$h = \sqrt{12^2 - 8^2}$$
> $$h = \sqrt{244 - 64} = \sqrt{180} = 8.94 \text{ feet}$$

Comment

Slant height is the diagonal distance from the top of a cone to its base.

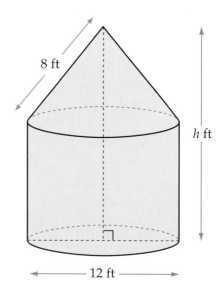

8 ft

h ft

12 ft

a. What mistake did Rosa make?

b. What is the correct answer? Show your work.

Putting Mathematics to Work

Preparing for the Closing

4. Compare your solutions for problems 1–3 with those of another pair of students. Together, write some advice for Lisa, Dwayne, and Rosa to help them avoid making similar mistakes in the future. Also, write about other mistakes all students need to avoid when solving problems using the Pythagorean theorem.

5. The length and width of a rectangle are p units and q units, respectively. Show how the Pythagorean theorem can be used to write an expression for the length of the diagonal in terms of p and q.

6. The length of the diagonal of a square is $\sqrt{2}$ times the length of its side.

   Use the Pythagorean theorem to help you explain why this statement is *always true*.

Skills

Solve.

a. $\$730 - \$5 - 40\cent =$

b. $\$730 - \$10 - 40\cent =$

c. $\$730 - \$50 - 40\cent =$

d. $\$735 + \$5 + 40\cent =$

e. $\$735 + \$10 + 40\cent =$

f. $\$735 + \$50 + 40\cent =$

Review and Consolidation

Consider each statement below and ask yourself the question, "Is this statement True or False?" Make a decision, and then provide an explanation for your choice using figures, algebra, and words.

1. The two legs of a right triangle measure 7" and 8". The hypotenuse measures 15".

2. The hypotenuse of a right triangle measures 15" and one of the legs of the triangle measures 12". The length of the third side cannot be calculated.

3. The width of a rectangular gate is 5 m and its height is 1.5 m. The longest diagonal strut across the gate measures 5 m 22 cm.

4. The length of the slant edge of a cone is known, as well as the diameter of the base of the cone. The perpendicular height of the cone can be calculated using this information.

Putting Mathematics to Work

5. If three numbers a, b, and c fit the Pythagorean theorem $c^2 = a^2 + b^2$, then they represent the side measures of a right triangle.

6. If three numbers a, b, and c (where $c > a$ and $c > b$) fit the inequality $c^2 < a^2 + b^2$, then they represent the side measures of an obtuse triangle.

Homework

1. Calculate the length of the diagonal of a rectangular gate with a length of 1 m and a height of 2 m. (Express your answer to the nearest centimeter.)

2. Chen was asked to complete the following problem, but unfortunately he made some mistakes. Figure out where Chen went wrong, and explain what he did wrong. Then complete the problem correctly.

"Calculate the side length of a square where the length of the diagonal is 5 ft."

Chen began his solution by sketching a figure like this:

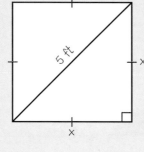

Then he wrote:

x + x = 5

Therefore, 2x = 5

x = 2.5

The side length of the square is 2.5 feet.

DISTANCE BETWEEN TWO POINTS

GOAL

To learn how to compute the distance between two points on the coordinate plane.

Work Time

1. Suppose you want to find the distance between point A at $(-2, 4)$ and point B at $(1, 1)$.

   a. On graph paper, plot the two points.

   b. Plot the point C at $(-2, 1)$ and draw the line segments AB, BC, and AC.

   c. What is unique about the resulting triangle? Based on your answer, explain how the coordinates for point C were chosen.

   d. Find the length of $\overline{AC}$ and $\overline{BC}$.

   e. Use the Pythagorean theorem to find the length of $\overline{AB}$.

When you apply the Pythagorean theorem to coordinate geometry, you can generalize using points (x_1, y_1) and (x_2, y_2).

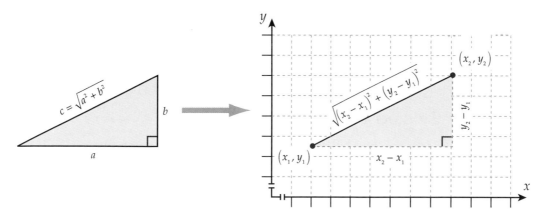

The result is known as the *distance formula*:

$$d = \sqrt{\left(x_2 - x_1\right)^2 + \left(y_2 - y_1\right)^2}$$

You can use the distance formula to find the distance between any two points on the coordinate plane.

2. Find the distance between each of these two points.

   a. (2, 3) and (7, 10)

   b. (5, 4) and (–3, –3)

   c. (5, –6) and (–2, –3)

   d. (–10, –3) and (–3, –5)

   e. How might you check to see if your answers are approximately correct?

3. Find the radius of a circle that has its center at (–3, 4) and given that the point (1, 7) lies on the circle.

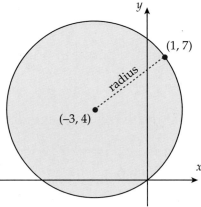

4. One hiker is 20 miles due west of the campsite and another hiker is 15 miles due south and 15 miles due east of the campsite. How far apart are they?

> **Hint:** Plot the points on a coordinate plane with the campsite at the origin.

5. A triangle has vertices *A* at point (12, 5), *B* at point (5, 3), and *C* at point (12, 1). Show that the triangle is isosceles.

6. Find the value of *x* if the points (1, 3) and (*x*, 9) are 13 units apart.

Preparing for the Closing

7. Suppose that the hikers in problem 4 were walking at 2 miles per hours. When would each one arrive at the camp site?

8. a. Create a problem similar to problem 3 that involves determining the value of the missing part of a figure on a coordinate grid.

   b. Calculate the answer on a separate piece of paper.

   c. Give the problem to your partner to solve.

   d. Discuss the results with your partner.

Skills

Solve:

a. $35 • 10   b. $35 • 20   c. $35 • 40   d. $35 • 80

e. $35 • 0.10   f. $35 • 0.20   g. $35 • 0.40   h. $35 • 0.80

i. $3.50 • 10   j. $0.35 • 20   k. $3.50 • 0.40   l. $0.35 • 80

Review and Consolidation

1. Find the distance between each of these two points.

a. $(2, 0)$ and $(-4, 0)$ b. $(-3, 0)$ and $(4, 0)$

c. $(0, -2)$ and $(0, -9)$ d. $(0, 8)$ and $(0, -4)$

e. $(1, 4)$ and $(8, 7)$ f. $(-4, -2)$ and $(6, -3)$

g. $(3, 3.4)$ and $(3, -9)$ h. $(-7, 7)$ and $(-3, -1)$

i. $(-6, -2)$ and $\left(-1\frac{2}{3}, -2\right)$ j. $\left(\frac{1}{2}, \frac{1}{4}\right)$ and $\left(-\frac{1}{2}, \frac{9}{4}\right)$

2. Find the distance between points A and B.

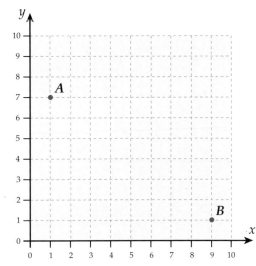

3. Write an expression that could be used to represent the distance between (x, y) and $(-2, 5)$.

1. Find the distance between each of these two points.

   a. (0, 0) and (5, 12)

   b. (0, 0) and (7, 24)

   c. (2, 8) and (6, 11)

   d. (−2, 5) and (2, 7)

   e. (4, 7) and (−8, −15)

   f. (8, 13) and (1, 10)

2. You leave your campsite and hike 7 miles due east then 9 miles due north. How far are you from the campsite?

3. Prove that the figure *ABCD* is a square.

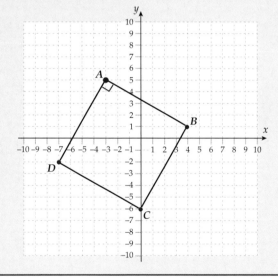

ONE- AND TWO-DIMENSIONAL MEASURES

GOAL

To learn about one- and two-dimensional measures, and to calculate the perimeters of polygons and the areas of rectangles, triangles, and composite shapes.

Jamal spent one weekend helping his grandfather lay bricks for a new walkway leading to the front door of their house.

"For this to look like a professional job, we have to measure as carefully as possible," explained Jamal's grandfather, Mr. Hakim.

He picked up one of the bricks. "A one-dimensional measure can be made with a tape measure, at least theoretically," said Mr. Hakim, taking a tape measure out of his pocket and stretching it across the brick.

"Here are some measurements we can make on this rectangular brick."

> **CONCEPT BOOK**
>
> See pages 231–238, 240–243, and 245–246.

These dimensions of a rectangle are called *length* and *width*, or *base* and *height*.	This distance across a rectangle (from vertex to vertex) is a *diagonal*.	The *perimeter* is the total distance around all of the edges.

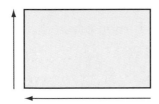 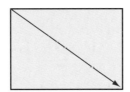 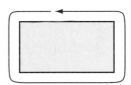

Comment A *dimension* is a measurable quality, such as length or height.

Mr. Hakim said, "This brick has a width of 4 inches and a length of 8 inches. The perimeter is 4 inches + 8 inches + 4 inches + 8 inches = 24 inches.

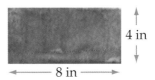

"Perimeter is a one-dimensional measure, so it can be represented as a straight line."

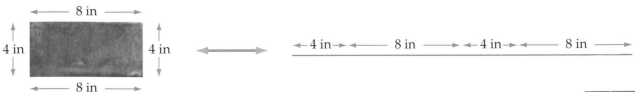

"A two-dimensional measure is the product of two one-dimensional measures," Mr. Hakim continued. "Area is an example of a two-dimensional measure.

"One way to determine the area of a rectangle is by direct measurement. You could cover the rectangle with square units and count them. You could also use the formula for area, $A = lw$ or $A = bh$, where l = length, w = width, b = base, and h = height.

"It is impossible to draw a straight line to represent area. Area is not one-dimensional; it is two-dimensional.

"Notice the difference between these equations for perimeter and area," Mr. Hakim pointed out, jotting the two equations on a piece of paper:

$P = 4 \text{ in} + 8 \text{ in} + 4 \text{ in} + 8 \text{ in} = 24 \text{ in}$

$A = 4 \text{ in} \bullet 8 \text{ in} = 32 \text{ in}^2$

"The units of measure are also different," noted Jamal. "The one-dimensional measure is inches; the two-dimensional measure is square inches."

"Very good," agreed Jamal's grandfather. "If you know the area of a rectangle, you can calculate the area of a triangle with the same base and height dimensions as the rectangle. We will need to do this for the borders of the walkway.

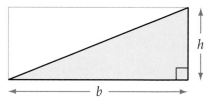

"The area of the triangle covers exactly one-half of the area of the rectangle.

"The formula for the area of a triangle is $A = \frac{1}{2}bh$, where b represents the base and h represents the height."

Jamal looked at his grandfather and pleaded, "Grandpa, can we please just get started?"

"Of course," said Mr. Hakim, laughing good-naturedly, "but now you see how important math can be in everyday life."

Work Time

1. Determine the perimeters and areas of the two shaded figures on the grid. Each square in the grid measures one square centimeter.

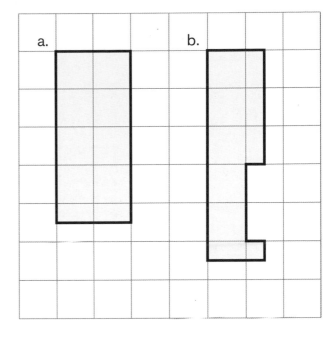

2. Calculate the perimeter of each figure below.

a.

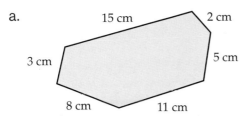

b.

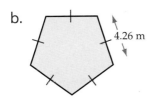

3. Calculate the area of this composite shape made up of two triangles and a rectangle. Write your answer in square feet.

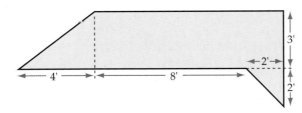

Comment

A *composite figure* is made up, or composed, of two or more smaller figures.

4. The areas have been given for these two rectangles. Calculate the missing dimension for each.

a.

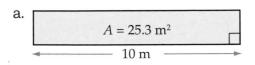

b.

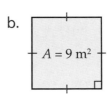

Preparing for the Closing ————————————————————

5. a. The triangles $\triangle ABC$, $\triangle ABD$, $\triangle ABE$, and $\triangle ABF$ shown on this coordinate plane have the same area. Say why.

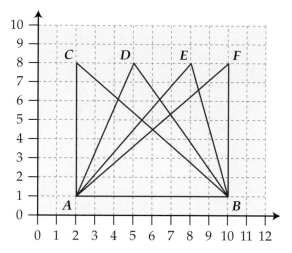

  b. Calculate the area of $\triangle ABC$.

6. The formula for the area of a triangle, $A = \dfrac{1}{2}bh$, may be determined from the formula for the area of a rectangle, $A = lw$.

  Say why. Sketch figures to support your answer.

7. a. Write a formula for calculating the area of a square of side length l.

  b. Say how your formula is related to the formula for the area of a rectangle.

8. Write a formula for the perimeter of a regular polygon with side length l. (Remember that in regular polygons all side lengths are equal.)

Skills

Calculate.

a. $\$976 \cdot 1 =$	**b.** $\$976 \cdot 2 =$	**c.** $\$976 \cdot 4 =$	**d.** $\$976 \cdot 8 =$
e. $\$976.50 \cdot 1 =$	**f.** $\$976.50 \cdot 2 =$	**g.** $\$976.50 \cdot 4 =$	**h.** $\$976.50 \cdot 8 =$
i. $\$976 \div 1 =$	**j.** $\$976 \div 2 =$	**k.** $\$976 \div 4 =$	**l.** $\$976 \div 8 =$
m. $\$976.50 \div 1 =$	**n.** $\$976.50 \div 2 =$	**o.** $\$976.50 \div 4 =$	**p.** $\$976.50 \div 8 =$

Review and Consolidation

1. Without using a calculator, find the perimeters for figures D and E below. Write each answer using an appropriate unit. (Look carefully at the units in each figure.)

a.

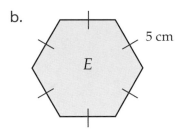

b.

   c. Lisa incorrectly calculated the perimeter for figure D as 292 mm. What common mistake could she have made?

2. What additional information do you need in order to calculate the area of this triangle?

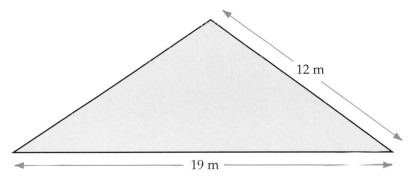

3. This rectangle has been partially covered in square tiles.

   a. How many more of these square tiles will be needed to completely cover the rectangle?

   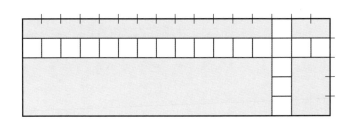

   b. What is the area of the rectangle?

4. This rectangle is twice as long as it is wide. Its area is 128 square inches. What are its dimensions?

   $A = 128$ sq inches

Homework

1. Calculate the area of each triangle. Write your answers in square centimeters.

   a.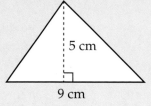

   b.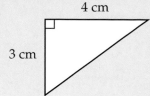

2. A rectangle has a length three times its width. The perimeter is 72 inches. Sketch the rectangle, and then calculate its dimensions.

3. Use the formula for the area of a rectangle to calculate the total area of the composite shape at right.

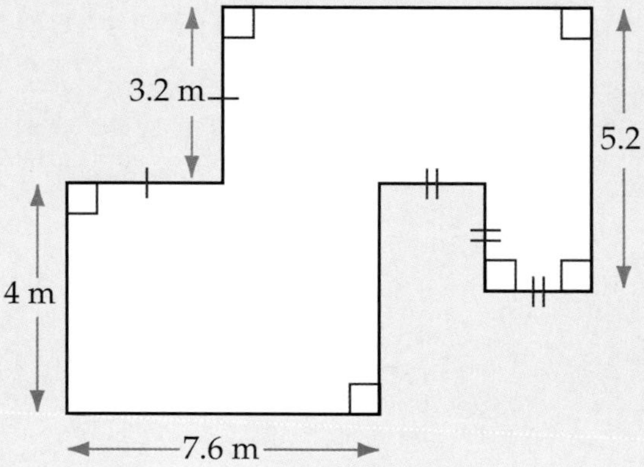

4. The area of a particular square is one-quarter of the area of the rectangle shown below.

   Calculate the perimeter of the square.

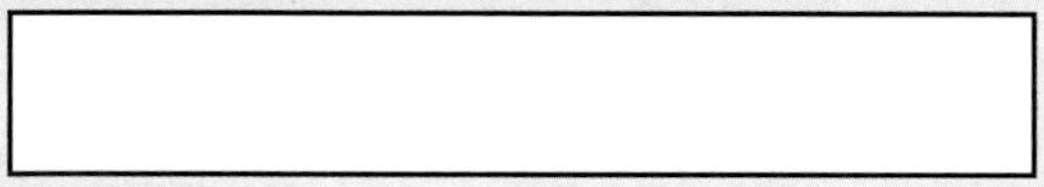

   50 m

   200 cm

AREA OF A POLYGON

GOAL

To calculate the area of any polygon.

"Guess what I just learned?" Rosa asked, coming out of the kitchen of the Valdez Restaurant to join Lisa, Jamal, Dwayne, and Chen in their study group.

CONCEPT BOOK

See pages 244–246.

"My brother, Carlos, showed me that you can use the formulas for the area of a rectangle and the area of a triangle to calculate the area of any polygon. You can 'divide' quadrilaterals into right triangles and rectangles, using perpendicular line segments," said Rosa.

On a piece of paper, Rosa drew a parallelogram and then used dashed lines to divide it into a rectangle and two right triangles.

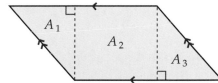

Area of Parallelogram = $A_1 + A_2 + A_3$

"Now, it's easy to find the areas of the rectangle and the triangles and add them together to get the area of the parallelogram. Here is another example," Rosa said, drawing a trapezoid.

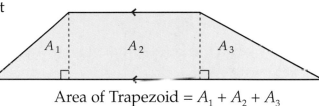

Area of Trapezoid = $A_1 + A_2 + A_3$

"For regular and irregular polygons with more than four sides, first draw any single diagonal of the polygon. Then, draw line segments that join each of the other vertices of the polygon to the diagonal and that are perpendicular to it. You can subdivide any trapezoids or rectangles that are formed in this process into right triangles, like this."

Regular Pentagon

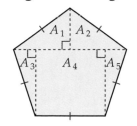

Irregular Polygons

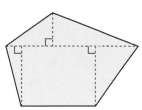
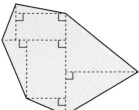

Area of Pentagon = $A_1 + A_2 + A_3 + A_4 + A_5$

Work Time

Use a calculator to solve the following problems.

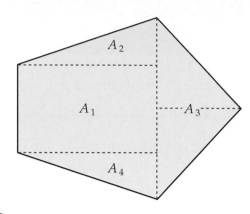

1. a. Which line segment measures do you need in order to calculate the area of the pentagon?

   b. Using a metric ruler, measure the appropriate line segments (in millimeters).

   c. Calculate the area of the pentagon.

   d. Compare your answer with that of another student. Are they the same? Say why or why not.

2. Calculate the area of this quadrilateral.

   Write your answer in square feet, and round it to two decimal places.

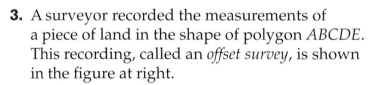

3. A surveyor recorded the measurements of a piece of land in the shape of polygon *ABCDE*. This recording, called an *offset survey*, is shown in the figure at right.

   a. Copy the figure.

   b. Sketch the sides of the polygon by connecting the points.

   c. Calculate the area of the piece of land, giving your answer to the nearest square meter.

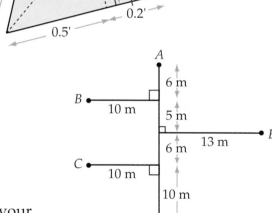

4. One side of an old schoolhouse is shown. This side needs to be painted.

   A 1-gallon can of paint costs $37.50 and will cover 42 square yards.

   a. How many gallons of paint are needed?

   b. What will the paint cost?

   c. What area can the leftover paint cover? (Write your answer to the nearest square yard.)

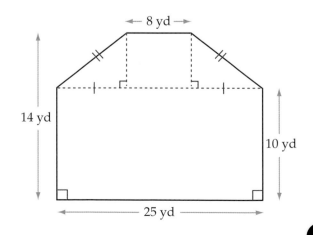

Preparing for the Closing

Think about and write a response to each of these statements.

5. One way to find the area of any quadrilateral is to divide it into four right triangles. Say why. Sketch a figure to show this.

6. To calculate the area of any polygon, all you need to know is the formula for the area of a right triangle. Say why.

7. Discuss with your partner how you can calculate the area of any polygon.

What shapes are useful for such calculations? What information do you need in order to calculate the areas of regular and irregular polygons?

Skills

Solve.

a. 32,370 + 4950 =   b. 323.70 + 4950 =   c. 32,370 + 49,500 =

d. 32,370 − 4950 =   e. 323.70 − 49.50 =   f. 323,700 − 49,500 =

Review and Consolidation

Use a calculator to solve the following problems.

1. Calculate the area of this quadrilateral. Write your answer in square feet.

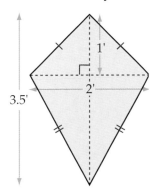

2. A surveyor needs to find a close approximation for the area of this irregularly shaped piece of land.

Describe a method that the surveyor could use to solve this problem.

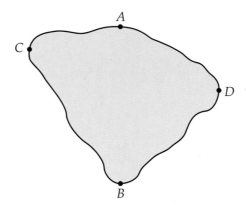

3. Measure the distance between a pair of parallel sides of this regular octagon. Measure the length of one side. Use a ruler scaled in millimeters.

Calculate the area of the octagon using your direct measurements.

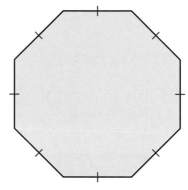

Homework

1. Calculate the area of this composite shape. Write your answer in square feet.

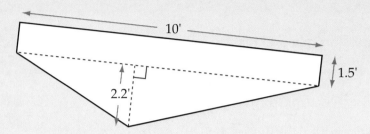

2. Calculate the area of this quadrilateral. Write your answer in square feet.

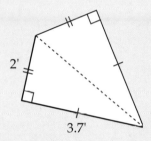

3. Calculate the area of this polygon. Write your answer in square centimeters.

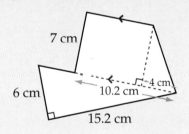

Hint: To find square roots, you can use the ☑ button on your calculator.

GOAL

To calculate the circumference and the area of a circle.

Circumference of a Circle and π

In all circles, the ratio of the circumference, C, to the diameter, d, is equal to π. (π is a Greek letter that is pronounced "pie.")

CONCEPT BOOK

See pages 238–240 and 245–246.

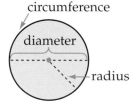

$$\frac{C}{d} = \pi \quad \text{or} \quad C = \pi d \quad \text{or} \quad C = 2\pi r$$

The value of π cannot be written down exactly, but it is between 3.14 and $\frac{22}{7}$. A calculator with a $\boxed{\pi}$ button uses an approximation for π that has many decimal places.

In geometric problems that involve circles, answers are often expressed in terms of π.

Example

The circumference of a circle with a diameter of 12 inches can be written as 12π inches.

Since $C = \pi d$ and $d = 12"$, $C = 12\pi"$.

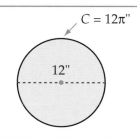

Area of a Circle and π

In all circles, the area of the circle is equal to the square of the radius times π. $A = \pi r^2$.

Example

The area of the shaded square is r^2.

Can you see why the area of the circle is less than $4r^2$?

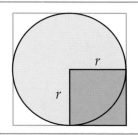

Work Time

1. Copy and complete the table below. For the fourth item, measure a circular item of your choice and fill in the measurements.

   Use a calculator and give all answers to two decimal places.

Circle	Circumference	Diameter	Circumference ÷ Diameter
Bicycle Wheel	31.4 in	10 in	
Soup Can	15.7 cm	5 cm	
Water Tank	39.25 ft	12.5 ft	
(Item of Your Choice)			

2. Consider your results for problem 1, and then answer the following questions.

   a. For any circle, what is the result when the measure of the circumference is divided by the measure of the diameter?

   b. The formula for the circumference of a circle is $C = \pi d$.

   Say how your results from problem 1 help you to understand this formula.

3. a. Measure the diameter of this circle in centimeters or in inches.

   b. Calculate the area of the circle. Use the approximation $\pi \approx 3.14$ for your calculation.

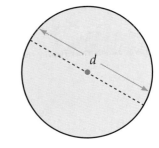

4. a. You can calculate the circumference of a circle if you know the radius. Say why.

   b. Calculate the circumference of the circle below. Use the approximation $\pi \approx 3.14$ for your calculation.

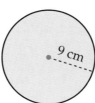

9 cm

5. a. You can calculate the diameter of a circle if you know the circumference. Say why.

$C = 42$ mm

b. Calculate the diameter of this circle using the $\boxed{\pi}$ button on your calculator.

Preparing for the Closing

Compare your answers with at least one other pair of students, and try to reach an agreement.

6. Discuss these statements with your partner. Decide whether each statement is true or false, and then write a justification for your choice.

a. When only the circumference of a circle is known, there is not enough information to determine the radius.

b. The circumference of a circle is doubled if the diameter is doubled.

c. When only the area of a circle is known, there is not enough information to determine the diameter.

d. The formula $C = 2\pi r$, where r stands for the radius of a circle, is equivalent to the formula $C = \pi d$, where d stands for the diameter of the circle.

Skills

Solve.

a. $36 \cdot 17 =$ b. $36 \cdot 34 =$ c. $360 \cdot 17 =$

d. $36 \cdot 27 =$ e. $36 \cdot 54 =$ f. $36 \cdot 37 =$

> **Hint:** Rewrite each problem as an easier problem that you can calculate in your head. For example, $13 \cdot 12$ can be written as $10(10 + 2) + 3(10 + 2)$.

Review and Consolidation

1. You can calculate the circumference of a circle if you know the diameter.

   a. Say why.

   b. Calculate the circumference of this circle.
      Write your answer in terms of π.

   c. Calculate the area of this circle.
      Write your answer in terms of π.

12"

2. Here are two figures of circles. Without using a calculator, find the missing measurements. Use the approximation π ≈ 3.14 for your calculations.

   a.

   15 m

   radius =
   circumference =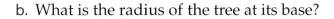

   b.

   17 m

   diameter =
   circumference =

3. In a California forest, there is a 2000-year-old Giant Sequoia tree with a diameter of 5.22 m at the base of its trunk.

   a. Sketch a figure.

   b. What is the radius of the tree at its base?

   c. What is the circumference of the tree at its base?
      (Use a calculator.)

4. Calculate the areas of the shaded parts of these circles.
   Write your answers in terms of π.

   a.

   ← 4' →

   b.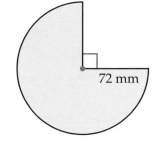

   72 mm

Homework

1. Calculate the circumference of each circle. Write your answers in terms of π.

   a.

   9"

   b.

   13"

2. Calculate the area of each circle. Write your answers in square meters. Use the approximation π ≈ 3.14.

   a.

   6 m

   b.
   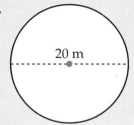
   20 m

3. The wheel of a toy car has a diameter of 2.6 cm. Find the following values. Use the approximation π ≈ 3.14, and express each answer to one decimal place.

   a. The radius of the wheel

   b. The circumference of the wheel

APPLYING PERIMETER AND CIRCUMFERENCE

GOAL

To apply geometry to real-life problems.

As you solve the Work Time problem, remember to:

- Read the word problem and understand the situation.

    What is the problem situation?

    Identify the quantities in the situation; name and label them.

- Represent the problem situation.

    Make figures with labels or pictures of relationships.

    Describe the problem situation in your own words.

    Make tables.

    Try simple numbers.

    Break the problem into smaller parts.

    Make up equations to express relationships.

- Understand the representations of other students.

- Answer questions about the problem situation.

CONCEPT BOOK

See pages 23–44
and 231–246.

Work Time

Work with a partner on this problem.

1. The figure on the next page is the design that Bruno, Rosa's favorite artist, made for a large wall-hanging.

    Bruno needs to know what it is going to cost him to buy enough gold braid to glue braid onto every curve and line of his design, including the outside edges.

    If Bruno's budget for the project is $5,000, will he be able to make his wall-hanging?

    Use the facts on the next page to solve the problem.

Putting Mathematics to Work

- Other than the braid, all materials needed to make the wall-hanging cost $1,000.

- The gold braid costs $12.45 per meter.

- The wall-hanging is a square of side length 10 m.

- The figure is drawn on 1-cm square-grid paper, with a scale of 1 cm to 1 m.

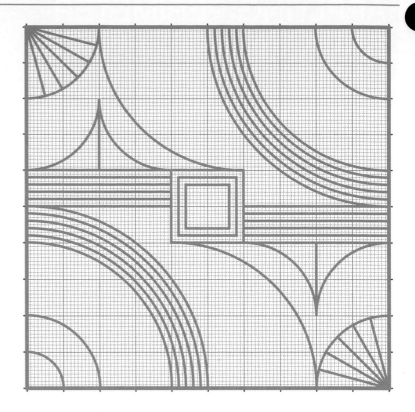

> **Comment**
>
> One centimeter on the grid paper equals one meter on Bruno's wall-hanging.

Present your solution clearly.

Show all of your work.

Preparing for the Closing

2. Discuss and compare your solution with another pair of students.

   Did you use the same methods to solve the problem?

   If not, how did your methods differ?

Skills

Estimate, and then solve.

   a. 77 ÷ 19 =   b. 780 ÷ 19 =   c. 8800 ÷ 19 =

   d. 98 ÷ 19 =   e. 1980 ÷ 19 =   f. 2980 ÷ 19 =

Review and Consolidation

1. In the bottom right corner of Bruno's wall-hanging design, there is a quarter circle with seven radii.

   a. Calculate the measure of the congruent angles formed by each pair of radii.

   Explain how you know you are correct.

   b. How many such angles would be needed to form a straight angle?

   Verify your answer using calculation.

2. The perimeter of a rectangle is 34 m, and the width of the rectangle is 5 m. What is the length of the rectangle?

3. How many times has a wheel of circumference 30 cm turned after it has rolled a distance of 10 m?

Homework

1. A 2 m piece of wire is cut into two pieces. The first piece is formed into a circle of diameter 23 cm, and the second piece is formed into a rectangle.

   a. Sketch a figure.

   b. Calculate the circumference of the circle.

   c. Find the dimensions of the rectangle, given that its length is three times its width.

   d. Calculate which has the greater area, the circle or the rectangle.

Putting Mathematics to Work

To learn how a one- or two-dimensional object can be moved in a plane.

One- or two-dimensional objects can change their position or size in a plane. Such changes are called *transformations*. In this lesson, you will learn about three types of transformations called *translation*, *reflection*, and *rotation*.

These are *congruent* transformations because the *object* (the initial figure) and its *image* (the final figure) are exactly the same size and shape after the change in position.

Translation

A transformation that moves an object a certain distance in any direction in a plane is called a *translation* (or *slide*).

In Quadrant I of this coordinate plane, every point in $\overline{PQ}$ has moved the same distance to form the image $\overline{P'Q'}$. Every point of triangle ABC has moved the same distance to form the image triangle $A'B'C'$.

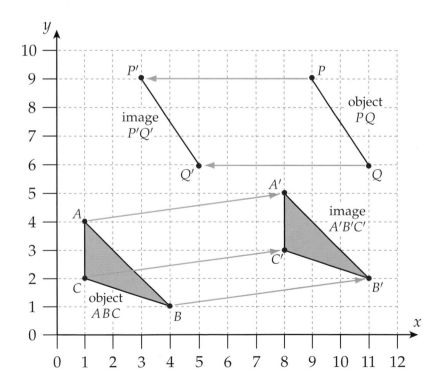

Reflection

A transformation that forms a mirror image of an object in a plane is called a *reflection* (or *flip*).

The line over which the object is transformed is called the *line of reflection*.

Every point of the quadrilateral *ABCD* is transformed an equal distance from the *y*-axis to form the mirror image *A'B'C'D'*.

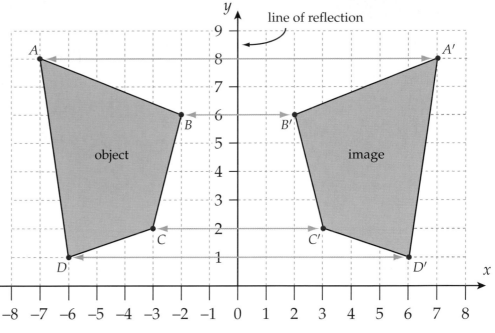

Rotation

A transformation that rotates an object around a fixed point is called a *rotation* (or *turn*).

The fixed point is called the *center of rotation*.

Rotations can be clockwise or counterclockwise.

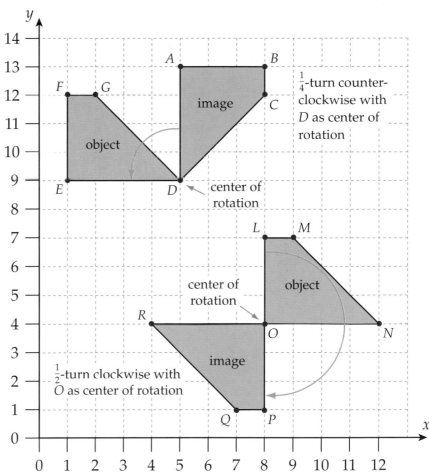

Work Time

Your teacher will give you copies of Handout 3: *Translations*, Handout 4: *Reflections*, and Handout 5: *Rotations* for use in problems 1–3.

1. Sketch the images that result when you perform the given translations on each of the objects. Then, write the coordinates of both the original and the translated points.

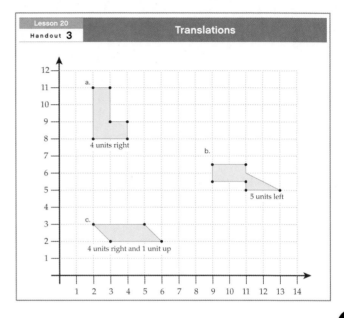

2. Sketch the images that result when you reflect each object using the given lines of reflection.

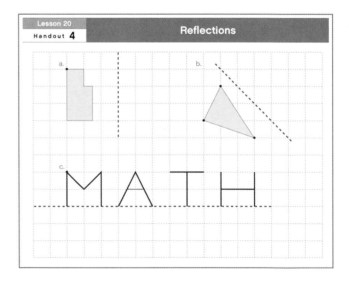

3. Sketch the images that result when you rotate each object 180° clockwise using the centers of rotation at point *D*.

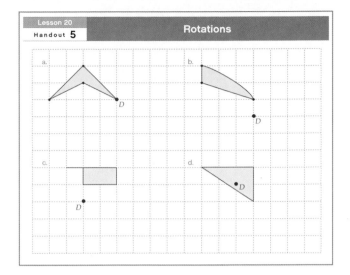

4. Consider this figure of triangle *ABC*.

For each transformation below, write the coordinates of the vertices of the image *A'B'C'*.

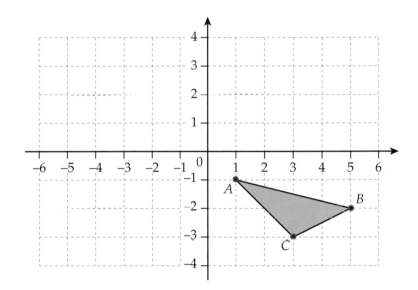

a. A translation of 4 units up and 3 units left.

b. A reflection with the vertical axis as the line of reflection

c. A rotation of 180° counterclockwise about the origin (0, 0)

5. In a translation, a line segment and its image are parallel, except when the translation is in the same direction as the line segment.

Sketch examples on a coordinate plane of translated line segments that explain what this statement means.

Preparing for the Closing

6. For all three transformations (translation, reflection, and rotation), the properties of length, angle measure, and area in two-dimensional figures are said to be *invariant* (or unchanging).

> **Comment**
>
> You will need to use a protractor and a ruler or a straightedge to help you with this problem.

Using a scalene triangle as your figure, make sketches to show what this means.

Skills

Solve.

a. ▢ • 41 = 2091

b. 51 • 8 • ▢ = 2040

c. 2040 ÷ 39 = ▢

d. 2040 ÷ 38 = ▢

e. 51 • 38 = ▢

f. 51 • 35 = ▢

Review and Consolidation

1. On a piece of graph paper:

a. Draw axes for x and y from –8 to 8. Plot the vertices of triangle ABC, where A has coordinates $(-6, -2)$, B $(-2, 1)$, and C $(-1, 5)$.

Construct each of the following images of triangle ABC.

b. Triangle $A'B'C'$ by reflection across the y-axis

c. Triangle $A''B''C''$ by reflection across the x-axis

d. Triangle $A'''B'''C'''$ by reflection across the line $y = x$

e. Write the coordinates of the image triangles in parts b–d.

2. Determine the unknown sides and angles in the following figures.

a. Translation: $\triangle ABC$ to $\triangle PQR$

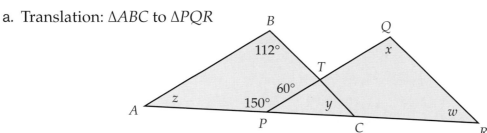

b. Rotation: $\triangle LMO$ to $\triangle XYO$, 240° counterclockwise about point O

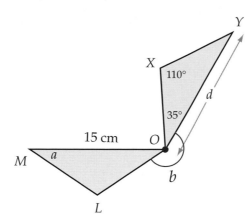

1. Chen sketched the following figures for his math homework. Describe the possible transformations he made to get each image from the given objects. Note that an answer could possibly involve more than one transformation.

a.

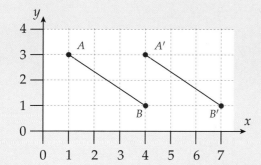

b.

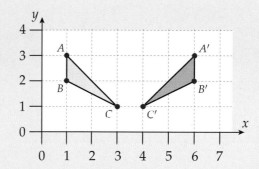

c.

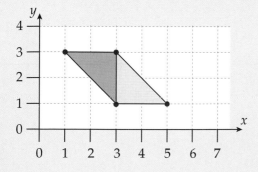

d.

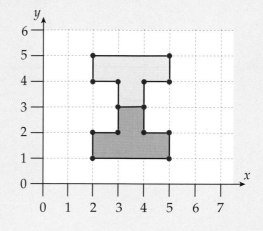

2. Copy each figure along with the given lines of reflection on a piece of graph paper. Sketch the reflection of each figure.

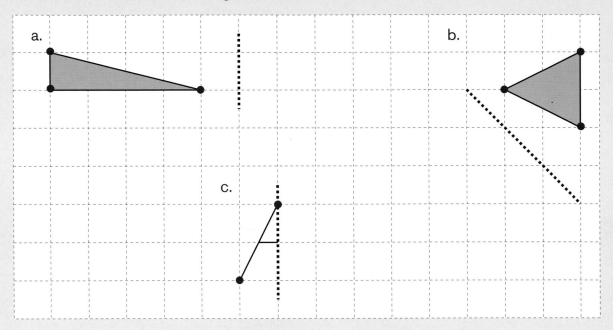

3. Copy each figure and its given center of rotation (shown as a dot) on graph paper. Draw the image of each after being rotated 90° clockwise about the center of rotation.

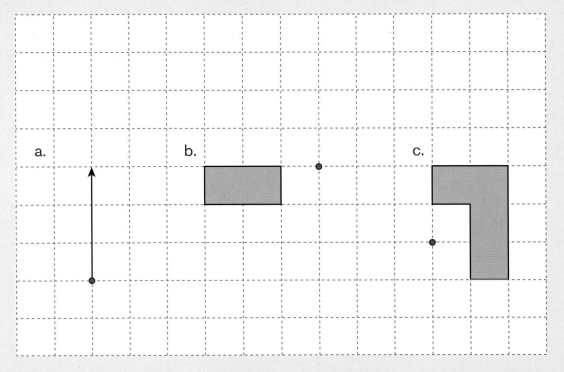

TESSELLATING POLYGONS

GOAL

To learn about tessellations of polygons, and to create a design for wrapping paper using a tessellation.

A *tessellation* is a repeating pattern of shapes that completely covers (or tiles) a plane.

A *regular tessellation* covers a plane with identical copies of just one regular polygon.

Here is the start of a tessellation that uses regular hexagons.

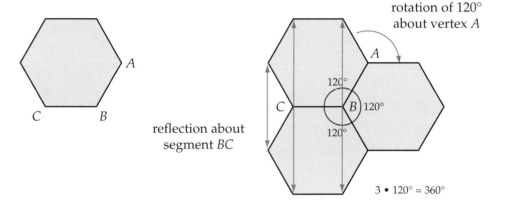

At each vertex within a tessellation, the sum of the angles is 360°. For this reason, some regular polygons will not tessellate.

For example, this figure shows you that regular pentagons do not tessellate.

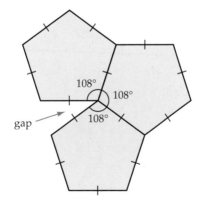

Putting Mathematics to Work

If a polygon tessellates, then it can be changed to make another shape that will also tessellate.

Example

You can modify a polygon by "cutting" a piece from one side and translating or rotating that piece to another place on the polygon.

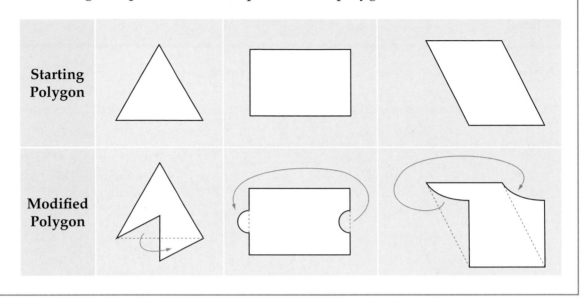

| Starting Polygon | | |
| Modified Polygon | | |

If you draw pictures on your modified polygon, you can create some really great designs!

Example

Here is an example of an irregular tessellation made with identical copies of just one "modified" (irregular) polygon.

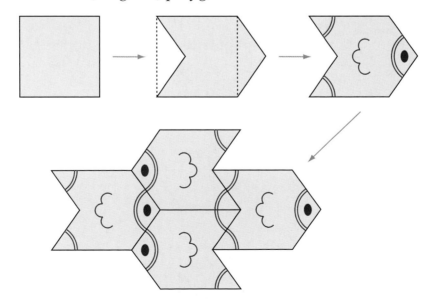

Work Time

Your task for this lesson is to use your knowledge of polygon shapes, transformations, and tessellations to create a design for wrapping paper. You will need:

- Paper and pencils to sketch your starting polygon and your ideas for the modified form
- Some cardstock to use for your modified polygon template
- Scissors
- A large sheet of plain paper on which to construct your tessellation
- Some colored pens or pencils

1. Choose and sketch a regular polygon.

2. Modify your polygon by "cutting" a shape from one side and "adding" it to the opposite side.

3. Construct a template of your modified polygon from a piece of cardstock.

4. Start in the top left corner of the large sheet of paper and trace around your template.

5. Using transformations (translations, reflections, rotations, or combinations of these), make congruent copies of your template in such a way that you form a tessellation.

Hint: Plan your tessellation before you trace around the shapes. Remember, you should have no gaps.

6. Color your tessellation to finish your design.

Preparing for the Closing

7. When you have completed your design, reflect on your work by asking yourself these questions:

- Does your design tessellate properly? How do you know?
- How many types of transformations did you use? Describe them.

8. Compare your design with those of other students.

Putting Mathematics to Work

Skills

Express each decimal as a percent.

a. 0.7   b. 0.07   c. 0.17   d. 0.017

e. 0.5   f. 0.05   g. 0.25   h. 0.65

Review and Consolidation

1. Try tessellating these block letters.

   a. Can you tessellate the letter C? Show why or why not.

   b. How about the letter F? Show why or why not.

   c. Find another letter in the alphabet that you can tessellate and show an example.

   d. Find a letter that you cannot tessellate and show why.

2. Ask your teacher for some pattern blocks in the shapes of squares, triangles, trapezoids, hexagons, rhombuses, or other polygons.

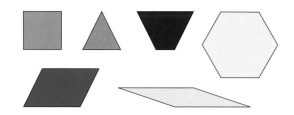

   a. Make patterns with the blocks, making certain you leave no gaps or spaces.

   b. Discuss the patterns with your partner.

- Which shapes fit together easily?

- Which shapes do not seem to fit with the others?

- Which shapes fit together to make a pattern that uses only one type of block?

- Which shapes fit together to make a pattern that uses two different types of blocks?

3. A square is made up of four 90° angles. Explain why a square can be tessellated.

4. a. What is the sum of the angles of any quadrilateral?

   b. Why does your answer mean that any quadrilateral to be tessellated?

5. An equilateral triangle is made up of three 60° angles. Explain why an equilateral triangle can be tessellated.

6. a. What is the sum of the angles of any triangle?

   b. Why does your answer mean that any triangle to be tessellated?

Homework

1. A regular pentagon is a shape that will not tessellate. Find another regular polygon that will not tessellate and make a sketch to illustrate. Use your knowledge of interior angles to explain this result.

2. Use the shape at right to form a tessellation by translating the shape left and right, and by reflecting it up and down.

3. For each of these tessellation patterns:

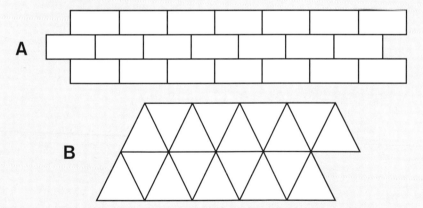

   a. Look at the polygon in the bottom left corner of each tessellation. Write the name of the tessellating polygon.

   b. Describe two different combinations of two transformations of the polygon that could form the tessellation.

Putting Mathematics to Work

GOAL

To learn about symmetry in simple figures and solids.

Symmetry in Two-Dimensional Shapes

Symmetry about a Line

Look at the shape below. You can see that the line of reflection divides it into two identical parts. Each part is the mirror image of the other.

The shape has *line symmetry*. The line of reflection is also called a *line of symmetry*.

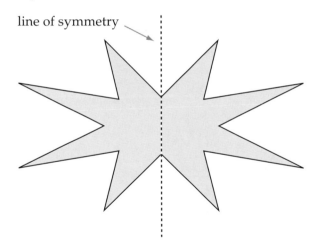

This particular shape also has another line of symmetry.

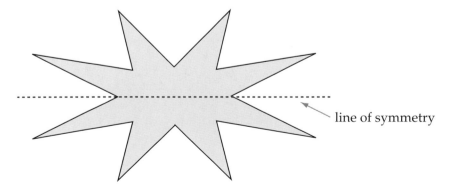

Two-dimensional shapes may have zero, exactly one, or more than one line of symmetry.

  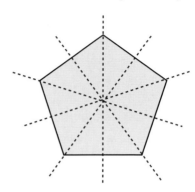

Symmetry about a Point

Look at the propeller shape below, consisting of three shaded segments. You can see that it can be rotated about its center point to form images that are exactly the same as the original object. The shape has *rotational symmetry*.

This particular shape has an *order 3* rotational symmetry. It will fit exactly onto the original shape three times (once for every 120° rotation) before it gets back to its starting position.

Order of symmetry can be 0, 2, or more than 2, but not 1.

This figure has neither rotational symmetry nor line symmetry.

This figure has order 2 rotational symmetry; it also has line symmetry.

 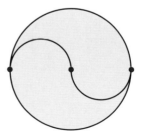

This figure has order 7 rotational symmetry; it also has seven lines of symmetry.

This figure has order 2 rotational symmetry but does not have line symmetry.

Symmetry in Three-Dimensional Shapes

Symmetry about a Plane

Look at the shape below. You can see that the plane divides the shape into two identical mirror images.

The shape has *plane symmetry*.

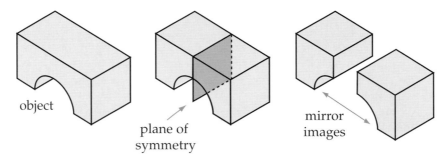

object

plane of
symmetry

mirror
images

This particular object also has another plane of symmetry.

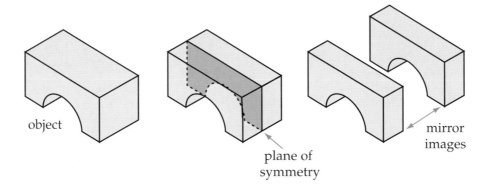

object

plane of
symmetry

mirror
images

Shapes can have zero, exactly one, or more than one plane of symmetry. For example, the rock has no planes of symmetry, the ant has one plane of symmetry, and the three-dimensional star has seven planes of symmetry.

Symmetry about a Line

Look at the shape below. You can see that if it is rotated 180° about the line, its image will sit exactly on the original shape. The line is called the *axis of rotation*.

This shape has order 2 rotational symmetry about this axis of rotation. (Remember that one rotation is equal to the amount an object has to turn to sit exactly on itself again. In this case, the rotation is 180°.)

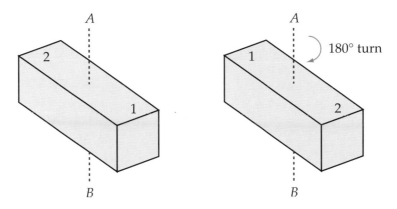

This particular shape has another axis of rotation. It has order 4 rotational symmetry about this axis. It takes a 90°-degree rotation for the object to sit exactly on itself again.

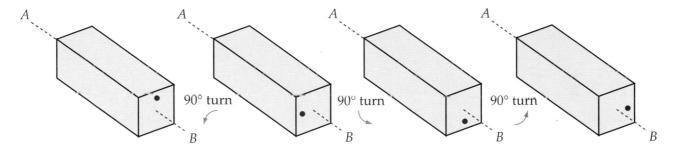

Your teacher will give you a copy of Handout 6: *Line and Plane Symmetry* to use with problems 1 and 4.

1. On the handout, mark all the lines of symmetry for each two-dimensional shape.

   a. Rectangle

   b. Regular hexagon

   c. Rhombus

   d. Isosceles triangle

2. In your notebook, sketch a shape (other than those in problem 1) that has:

   a. Zero lines of symmetry

   b. One line of symmetry

   c. Two lines of symmetry

3. Sketch a figure of each of the following shapes. Decide whether each shape has rotational symmetry about its center, and, for those that do, write the order.

   a. Parallelogram

   b. Isosceles triangle

   c. Equilateral triangle

   d. Regular pentagon

   e. Square

   f. Scalene triangle

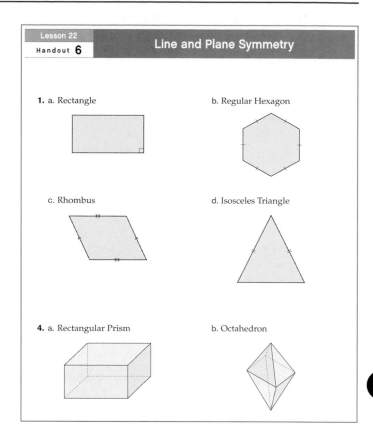

Lesson 22
Handout 6

Line and Plane Symmetry

1. a. Rectangle   b. Regular Hexagon

   c. Rhombus   d. Isosceles Triangle

4. a. Rectangular Prism   b. Octahedron

4. On the handout, shade in the horizontal plane of symmetry for each figure.

    a. Rectangular prism

    b. Octahedron (a regular eight-sided solid)

Preparing for the Closing

5. Discuss your results for problem 1 with a partner. What properties of each shape determine the lines of symmetry?

6. Lisa claims that the number of lines of symmetry of a plane figure is equal to the order of rotational symmetry of the figure.

    Is Lisa correct? Explain your answer.

Skills

Express each percent as a decimal.

    a. 1%   b. 1.9%   c. 1.09%   d. 19%

    e. 33%   f. 3.3%   g. 33.3%   h. 33.33%

Review and Consolidation

1. Sketch a two-dimensional shape (different from those in Work Time problem 3) that has:

    a. Rotational symmetry but no line symmetry

    b. Line symmetry but no rotational symmetry

    c. Rotational symmetry of order 2

    d. Rotational symmetry of order 5

2. What is the order of rotational symmetry of each shape?

a.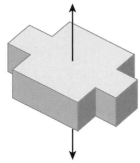

b.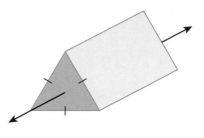

1. Write your name in capital letters. Draw all possible lines of symmetry on each letter.

2. Are there any capital letters of the alphabet that do not have at least one line of symmetry? If so, list them and say why.

3. Are there any capital letters of the alphabet that have rotational symmetry? If so, list them and give the order of symmetry.

4. How many planes of symmetry does each shape have?

a. Rectangular Prism

b. Rectangular Pyramid

c. Cone

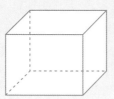
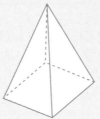

DEFINING CONGRUENCE

GOAL

To understand congruence, and to test figures for congruence using transformations: translation, rotation, and reflection.

Congruent figures are the same shape and size as each other.

CONCEPT BOOK

See pages 215, 218, and 243.

The symbol for "is congruent to" is ≅.

The statement:

quadrilateral $ABCD$ ≅ quadrilateral $PQRS$

means that:

- Point A corresponds to point P, B to Q, C to R, and D to S.

- All corresponding sides are the same length.

- All corresponding angles have the same measure.

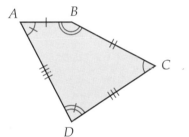 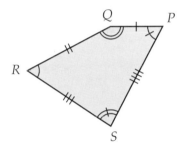

To test whether any two quadrilaterals $ABCD$ and $PQRS$ are congruent, you can move $PQRS$ to see if it fits exactly onto $ABCD$ by following these three steps:

1. Slide (or translate) $PQRS$, without rotating it, until point P sits on top of corresponding point A.

In this case, $PQRS$ moves horizontally to the left.

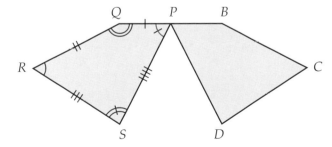

2. Then rotate *PQRS* about the point *P* until side *PQ* lies along corresponding side *AB*.

In this case, the angle of rotation is 180°.

Since $\overline{AB} = \overline{PQ}$, point *Q* should sit on top of the corresponding point *B*.

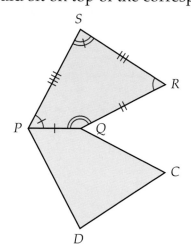

3. Then reflect *PQRS*, using line *PQ* as the line of reflection.

In this case, the quadrilaterals are congruent, so points *R* and *S* will sit on top of corresponding points *C* and *D*.

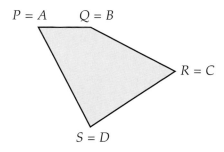

If *PQRS* ends up sitting exactly on *ABCD*, then the quadrilaterals are congruent.

Note that you do not always need to perform three transformations to show congruency—sometimes you can show it with fewer transformations.

Work Time

1. Match the congruent pairs of polygons.

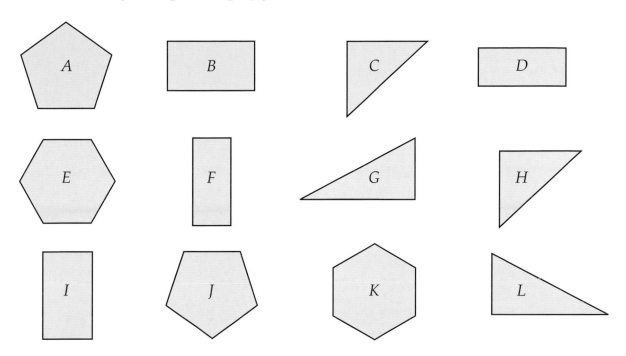

2. Look at the polygons in problem 1. You can think of figure *J* as the congruent image of figure *A* and figure *H* as the congruent image of figure *C*.

Which one transformation do you need to use, translation, reflection, or rotation, in order to exactly place:

a. Figure *A* onto figure *J*

b. Figure *C* onto figure *H*

3. These pentagons are congruent.

a. List the pairs of corresponding sides and corresponding angles.

b. Write a congruence statement for the pentagons using the symbol for congruence.

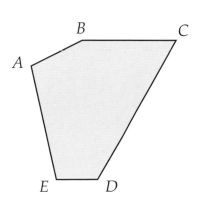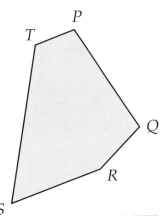

4. Quadrilateral $ABCD \cong$ quadrilateral $PQRS$.

    a. Sketch a figure of two possible quadrilaterals based on the statement above. Label the vertices.

    b. List the corresponding equal angles.

    c. List the corresponding equal sides.

5. Is triangle ABC congruent to triangle $A'B'C'$?

    Make appropriate measurements to provide evidence for your decision.

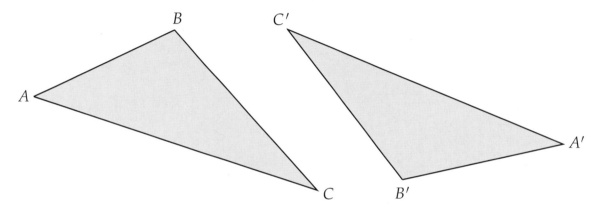

Preparing for the Closing

6. Only one pair of congruent figures in problem 1 has figures that are in the same orientation. Which pair is it?

7. Two triangles both have side lengths of 10 cm and 8 cm and an angle of 120°. Explain why they are not necessarily congruent.

8. a. Dwayne tells Rosa that to test whether or not two figures are congruent, she only needs to measure the corresponding angles. Is Dwayne's statement true or false? Justify your answer.

    b. Rosa tells Dwayne that when he tests for congruence in polygons, the order in which he writes the letters of the vertices is very important. Is Rosa's statement true or false? Justify your answer.

Skills

Calculate.

a. 6% of 600 b. 16% of 600 c. 66% of 600 d. 66% of 6000

e. 12% of 600 f. 48% of 600 g. 33% of 60 h. 6.6% of 6000

Review and Consolidation

1. In each of the following sets, no more than two of the figures are congruent.

Say which figures are congruent in each set.

Comment

The figures have been drawn so that they look the same, even if they are not.

a.

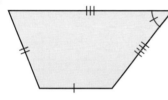 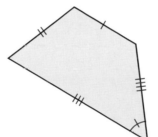 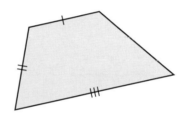

b.

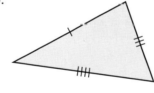 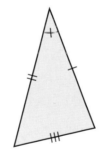 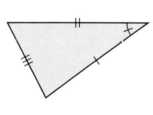

c.

 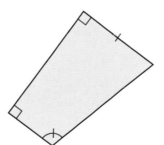 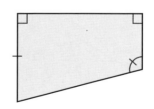

2. Describe the transformations that are needed to get each triangle from the start to the finish. In each case, there is more than one answer, with one of the possible answers requiring only one transformation.

a.

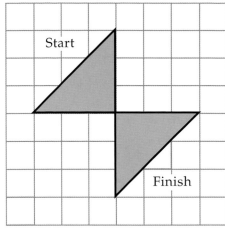

b.

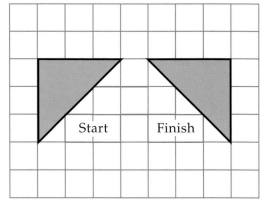

c.

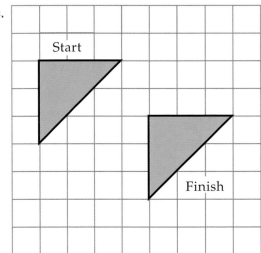

d.

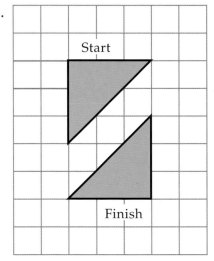

3. Given that each of these figures shows a pair of congruent triangles, find the value of the unknown sides or angles.

a.

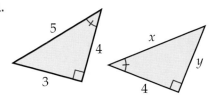

b.

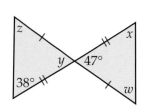

c.

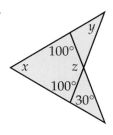

Homework

1. Triangle *RST* is scalene. It is congruent to triangle *XYZ*.

   a. Express this congruence relationship using symbols.

   b. Sketch a figure of two possible triangles *RST* and *XYZ*. Label the vertices.

   c. List the corresponding equal angles.

   d. List the corresponding equal sides.

2. For each congruent pair:

   • Label all the angles in both figures.

   • Calculate the size of angle *x*.

   • Draw congruence marks on both figures to show which sides are equal.

   a. $\overline{AB} = \overline{RS}, \overline{BC} = \overline{SP}$

   $\angle A = 135°$

   $\angle B = 118°$

   $\angle C = 64°$

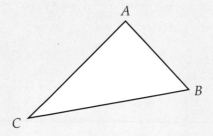
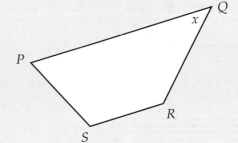

   b. $\overline{AC} = \overline{PR}$

   $\angle B = \angle Q = 55°$

   $\angle A = \angle P = 85°$

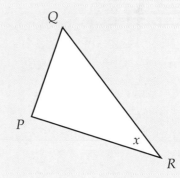

GOAL

To calculate the volume and the surface area of a rectangular prism.

Lisa, Rosa, Jamal, Chen, and Dwayne were at Dwayne's house studying three-dimensional measure.

"Okay," Lisa began. "We know that *volume* is a measure of the space inside a three-dimensional object.

One way to measure the volume of three-dimensional objects is by counting the number of cubic units that fit inside an object."

"Wait a minute!" interrupted Dwayne. He jumped up and left the room. He came back carrying a toy bucket. "My little brother's building blocks," he explained.

He took twelve square blocks out of the bucket and arranged six of the blocks in a 2 × 3-block rectangle. He then layered the remaining six blocks on top of the first six.

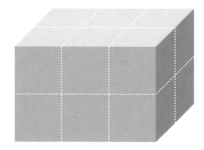

"These twelve cubes form a rectangular prism. The volume of this prism is 12 cubic units. *Cubic units* (cubes with a side length of one unit) are used as the units of volume, because cubes stack exactly together," said Dwayne.

"You can also calculate the volume of a rectangular prism by multiplying the base area by the perpendicular height: *volume* equals area of base times height," offered Chen as he wrote $V = Ah$. He turned to Rosa and challenged, "The linear dimensions of a rectangular prism are length, width, and height. Can you think of a formula for volume that uses all three one-dimensional measures?"

Rosa did not hesitate. "Since $V = Ah$, and $A = lw$, it follows that $V = lwh$."

CONCEPT BOOK

See pages 249–252.

"In class, we also learned about surface area," Jamal reminded the group. "The *surface area* of a rectangular prism is the sum of the areas of all *faces* (or sides) of the prism."

Dwayne dug into the bucket and pulled out a rectangular block. "Rectangular prisms have six faces. The opposite faces of a rectangular prism are the same, or congruent. We could use that information to calculate the surface area."

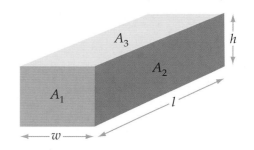

The surface area is:

$$S = 2(A_1 + A_2 + A_3) \text{ or } S = 2(wh + lh + lw).$$

As he was putting the blocks away, Dwayne started to laugh. "Who would have guessed that I'd be playing with blocks at my age?"

Comment

A *rectangular prism* is a three-dimensional figure, the base of which is a rectangle and the sides of which are parallelograms.

Work Time

1. Which shape at right has a greater volume, and by how much?

2. Calculate the volume of this rectangular prism.

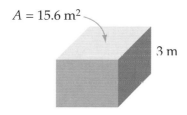

$A = 15.6 \text{ m}^2$

3 m

3. Calculate the volume of each rectangular prism. Write your answers in cubic meters.

a.

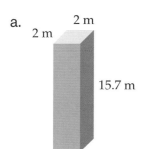

2 m
2 m
15.7 m

b.

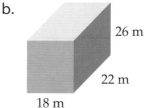

26 m
22 m
18 m

4. Calculate the total surface area for each prism in problem 3.

Preparing for the Closing

5. The volume of a rectangular prism can be calculated by multiplying its three dimensions of length, width, and height. Say why.

6. The height of a rectangular prism can be calculated if the volume and the area of the base are known. Say why, and support your answer with at least one example.

7. Say why the formula for calculating the surface area of a rectangular prism is:

$$S = 2(wh + lh + lw)$$

Skills

Solve.

    a. 13% of 79

    b. 26% of 79

    c. 2.6% of 79

    d. 13% of 179

    e. 39% of 179

    f. 3.9% of 179

    g. 13% of 279

    h. 1.3% of 279

    i. 10.3% of 279

Review and Consolidation

1. Calculate the volume of each box, and then write the letters of the boxes in order of volume, from largest to smallest.

    a.

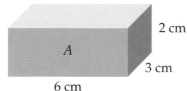

    b.

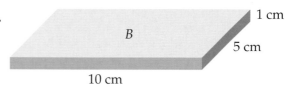

    c.

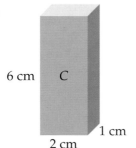

    d.

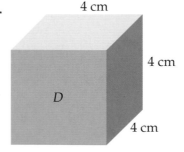

2. A rectangular prism has a length of 5 cm, a width of 3 cm, and a height of 4 cm.

   a. What is its volume?

   b. What is its volume if the length is doubled?

   c. What is the volume of the original prism if the width is doubled?

   d. What is the volume of the original prism if the height is halved?

3. A rectangular prism has a height of 12 units, a length of 3 units, and a width of 4 units.

   a. Calculate the volume of the prism.

   b. Calculate the surface area of the prism.

4. A rectangular prism with a square base is called a *square prism*. If a square prism has a volume of 80 cubic units, what could its dimensions be?

Homework

Complete all problems without using a calculator.

1. Which shape has a greater volume, and by how much?

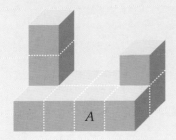 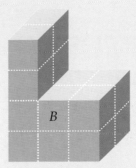

2. A fish tank is a rectangular prism with a length of 50 cm, a width of 30 cm, and a height of 20 cm. What is its volume?

3. Calculate the volume and surface area of each prism. Write your answers using the appropriate units.

   a.
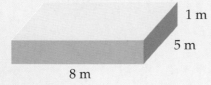

1 m
5 m
8 m

   b.
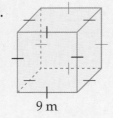

9 m

GOAL

To calculate the volume and surface area of parallel solids.

Parallel solids are three-dimensional objects that have congruent *cross-sections*.

CONCEPT BOOK

See pages 249–253.

> ### Comment
> A *cross-section* is the face that results from slicing a solid shape.

When you slice anywhere through the parallel solid, parallel to the base, you will see congruent shapes.

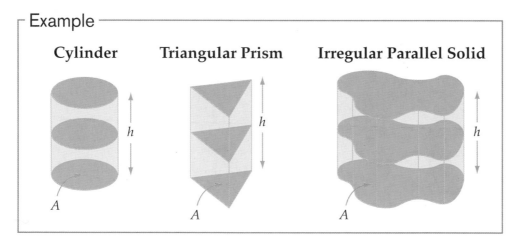

— Example —

Cylinder   **Triangular Prism**   **Irregular Parallel Solid**

The figure shown at right is not a parallel solid.

The formula for the volume of a parallel solid is $V = Ah$, where A is the area of the base and h is the perpendicular height.

When you multiply an area (two-dimensional) measure by a linear (one-dimensional) measure, the result is a volume (three-dimensional) measure.

The *rectangular prism* is a special kind of parallel solid, because any of its three linear dimensions can be used as the height.

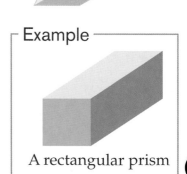

— Example —

A rectangular prism

Surface Area

The surface area of a parallel solid can be found by "unwrapping" or taking apart the faces of the solid and laying them flat.

The total surface area of a parallel solid equals the sum of the surface areas of all its parts.

Example

Here is a rectangular prism that has been "unwrapped."

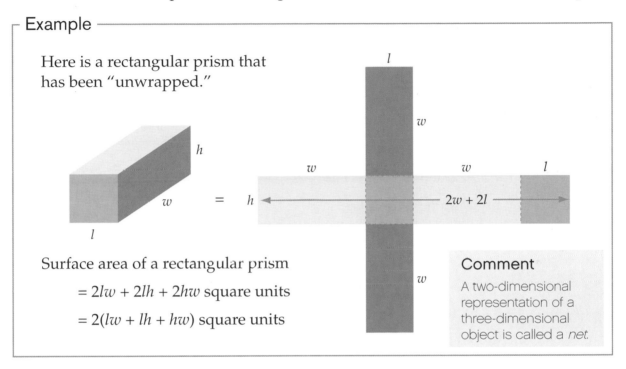

Surface area of a rectangular prism

$= 2lw + 2lh + 2hw$ square units

$= 2(lw + lh + hw)$ square units

Comment

A two-dimensional representation of a three-dimensional object is called a *net*.

Example

The surface area of a triangular prism = area of top + area of base + area of sides.

Here is a triangular prism that has been "unwrapped."

For the prism shown:

$S = 15.6 + 15.6 + 3(14 \cdot 6)$

$= 283.2 \text{ in}^2$

(14 • 6 is multiplied by 3 because there are three congruent sides.)

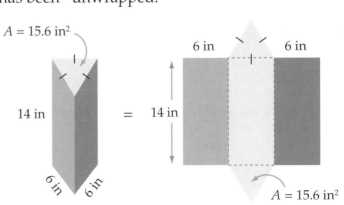

Surface area is a two-dimensional measure that is written in square units.

Work Time

Use a calculator to help you complete the calculations in these problems.

1. For this triangular prism:

    a. Write how to calculate the area of the base.

    b. Write how to calculate the volume.

    c. Write a formula that calculates the volume of any triangular prism in terms of its linear dimensions.

    d. Calculate the volume of this triangular prism.

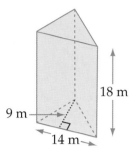

Comment

A *triangular prism* is a parallel solid with a triangle for a base and sides that are parallelograms.

2. For this cylinder shown:

    a. Explain why it is a parallel solid.

    b. Write how to calculate the area of the base.

    c. Write how to calculate the volume.

    d. Write a formula that calculates the volume of any cylinder in terms of its linear dimensions.

    e. Calculate the volume of this cylinder. Write your answer in terms of π.

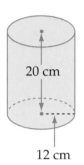

Comment

A *cylinder* is a parallel solid with a circular base.

3. Calculate the height of this rectangular prism given that the volume of the prism is 500 in³.

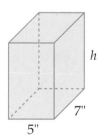

4. Calculate the height of this parallel solid.

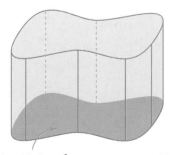

$A = 98.5 \text{ cm}^2$ $V = 1576 \text{ cm}^3$

5. a. Sketch the "unwrapped" faces for this parallel solid.

b. Calculate the total surface area.

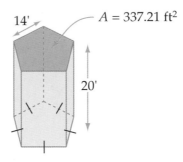

14' $A = 337.21$ ft^2

20'

Preparing for the Closing

6. Jamal's grandmother poured 500 cm^3 of water into a vase in the shape of a parallel solid. What could Jamal do to calculate the area of its irregular-shaped cross-section?

7. Two parallel solids have the same base area and the same height.

a. Do they have the same volume?

b. Do they have the same surface area?

c. Do they have the same shape?

Skills

Solve.

a. Dwayne bought a pair of jeans for $50. The sales tax is 6% of the cost. How much did Dwayne pay for the jeans?

b. The usual price for a compact disc is $25. On sale, the CD was sold at a discount of 12%.

What was the sale price of the CD?

Review and Consolidation

The formula for the volume of a parallel solid is $V = Ah$. Use your calculator and the formula to complete the calculations.

1.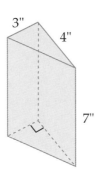

4 cm

15 cm²

$V = Ah$
$V = 15 \cdot \boxed{}$
$V = \boxed{}$ cm³

2.

32 mm

261.7 mm²

$V = Ah$
$V = \boxed{} \cdot \boxed{}$
$V = \boxed{}$ mm³

3.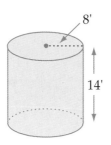

3"
4"
7"

$V = Ah$
$V = \boxed{} \cdot \boxed{}$
$V = \boxed{}$ in³

4.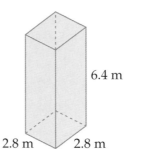

6.4 m

2.8 m   2.8 m

$V = Ah$
$V = \boxed{} \cdot \boxed{}$
$V = \boxed{}$

5.

8'
14'

$V = Ah$
$V = \boxed{} \cdot \boxed{}$
$V = \boxed{}$

6.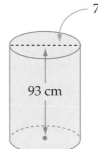

72 cm

93 cm

$V = Ah$
$V = \boxed{} \cdot \boxed{}$
$V = \boxed{}$

7. Show how to use the appropriate formulas to calculate the surface area and volume of the rectangular prism at right.

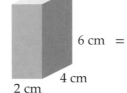

6 cm =

2 cm   4 cm

6 cm

4 cm

2 cm

Homework

1. Calculate the volume of each parallel solid.

a.

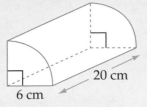

20 cm

6 cm

b.

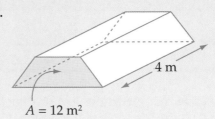

4 m

$A = 12$ m^2

2. Calculate the height of each solid.

a.

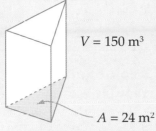

$V = 150$ m^3

$A = 24$ m^2

b.

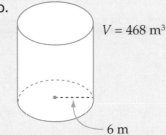

$V = 468$ m^3

6 m

3. Use the appropriate formulas to calculate the volume and surface area of a rectangular prism with length 12", height 6", and width 10".

GOAL

To calculate the volume of a point solid.

Point solids are three-dimensional objects with cross-sections that are similar but not congruent. The cross-sections decrease at a constant rate from the base to a point called the *apex*.

CONCEPT BOOK

See pages 253–254.

A *cone* is a point solid with a circular base.
A square-based *pyramid* is a point solid with a square base.

Example

Cone	Square-Based Pyramid	Point Solid with Irregular-Shaped Base

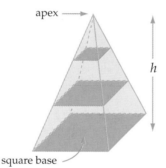
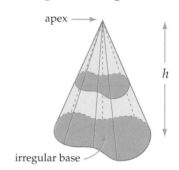

| If you slice anywhere through the cone, parallel to the base, you will see a circle. All circles are similar. | If you slice anywhere through the pyramid, parallel to the base, you will see a square. All squares are similar. | If you slice anywhere through the solid, parallel to the base, you will see similar shapes. |

The volume of all point solids is given by the formula $V = \frac{1}{3}Ah$.

In the formula, A represents the base area and h represents the perpendicular height. The base area can be calculated for some point solids. To find the volume of an object with an irregular base, you would need to estimate the area of the base, using an approximation method such as counting squares.

Work Time

1. For this cone:

   a. Write a description of how to calculate the base area
by using its linear dimensions.

   b. Write a formula for calculating the volume of a cone.

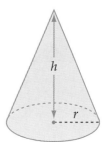

2. For this rectangular-based pyramid:

   a. Write a description of how to calculate the
base area by using its linear dimensions.

   b. Write a formula for calculating the volume
of a rectangular pyramid.

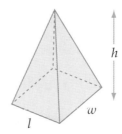

3. Another name for a triangular-based pyramid is *tetrahedron*.
For this tetrahedron:

   a. Write a description of how to calculate the area
of the base by using its linear dimensions.

   b. Write a formula for calculating the volume
of a tetrahedron.

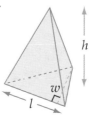

4. Calculate the volume of each point solid.

a.

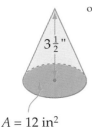

$3\frac{1}{2}"$

$A = 12$ in²

°b.

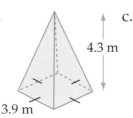

4.3 m

3.9 m

c.

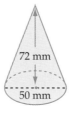

72 mm

50 mm

5. The dimensions of a rectangular prism are length = 14", width = 9", and height = 12".
A rectangular pyramid has the same base dimensions and the same height as the prism.
Calculate the volume of the pyramid.

Preparing for the Closing

6. Discuss with your partner how you calculate the base area of point solids.
Think about the information you need in each case, and give examples.
Write a statement that summarizes your discussion.

7. When the bases and heights are the same, what can you say about the volume of a parallel solid compared to the volume of a point solid? Justify your answer.

Skills

Calculate an equivalent percent for each of the following. Use any method, but show your work.

   a. Three out of five students have read *Monster*.

   b. Three out of eight students have read *The Outsiders*.

   c. Eight out of twelve students have seen the movie *Charlie and the Chocolate Factory*.

   d. Only one out of twelve students has read the book on which that movie was based.

   e. Four out of twenty students participate in basketball.

   f. Seven out of ten students have a skateboard.

Review and Consolidation

The formula for the volume of a point solid is $V = \frac{1}{3}Ah$.

Complete the steps in problems 1–3 to calculate the volume of each point solid.

1.

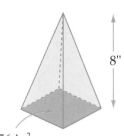

56 in²

$V = \frac{1}{3}Ah$

$V = \frac{1}{3} \cdot \boxed{} \cdot \boxed{}$

$V = \boxed{} \text{ in}^3$

2.

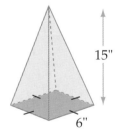

6"

$V = \frac{1}{3}Ah$

$V = \frac{1}{3} \cdot \boxed{} \cdot \boxed{}$

$V = \boxed{}$

3.

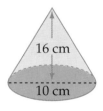

16 cm

10 cm

$V = \frac{1}{3}Ah$

$V = \boxed{} (\boxed{}) \cdot \boxed{}$

$V = \boxed{}$

4. The end of this square-based pyramid is cut off to make a vase. The vase is going to be filled with water.

How much water will it hold?

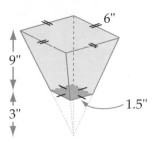

---

1. Calculate the volume of each point solid.

a.

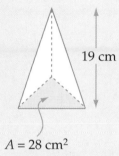

19 cm

$A = 28$ cm^2

b.

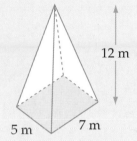

12 m

5 m   7 m

2. Calculate the volume of a cone with a height of 4" and a diameter of 2". Write your answer in terms of π.

3. A pyramid has a base area of 28 square inches and a volume of 140 cubic inches. Calculate the height of the pyramid.

To investigate polyhedrons.

Consider this rectangular prism:

CONCEPT BOOK

See pages 249–254

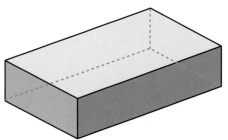

Imagine that the prism is cut open and flattened out.

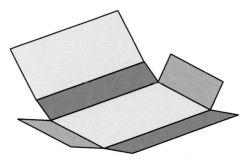

The result is a *net* that clearly shows all the faces and edges. Notice that in a net diagram, edges are matched to edges.

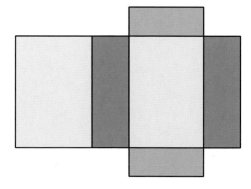

The net diagram of a polyhedron is a two-dimensional plan of the three-dimensional solid. *Polyhedrons* are geometric solids whose surfaces are all polygons.

Platonic solids are a special set of polyhedrons whose faces are all congruent, regular polygons.

Here are the Platonic solids and their nets.

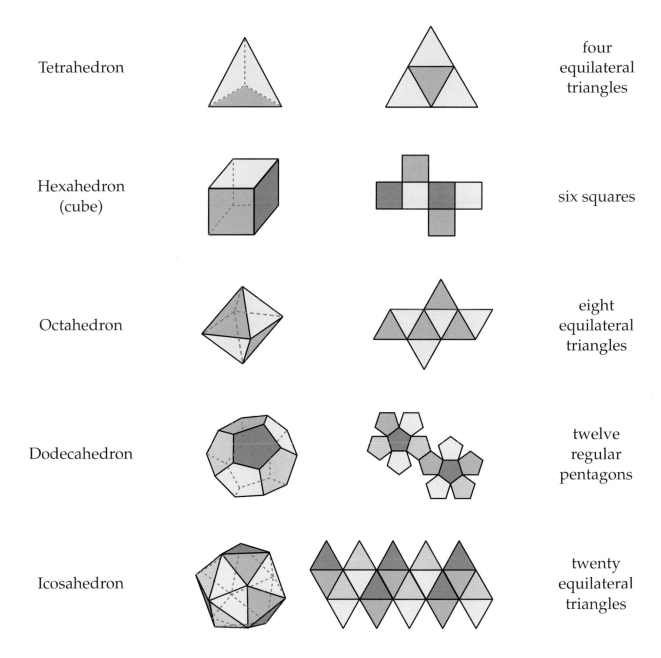

Tetrahedron			four equilateral triangles
Hexahedron (cube)			six squares
Octahedron			eight equilateral triangles
Dodecahedron			twelve regular pentagons
Icosahedron			twenty equilateral triangles

Other polyhedrons can be built by combining simple shapes or by cutting one shape out of another.

Work Time

1. This net diagram of a cube uses six squares. Each square represents one face of the cube. All the dimensions are equal. Check that the net makes a cube by recreating it on grid paper, cutting it out, and then folding it up.

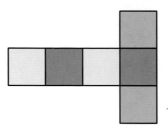

2. a. The following net diagrams show all the possible ways of arranging six squares. Your task is to decide which of these are nets for cubes and which are not.

   How many can you find?

   b. Using grid paper, copy those net diagrams that you decide represent cube nets.

   c. Cut out your nets. Test whether or not you were correct by folding up each net to see if it makes a cube.

   d. Devise a classification system for cube nets.

3. The introduction to this lesson illustrates one possible way of showing the net of Platonic solids.

Sketch at least two more nets for each Platonic solid.

Label each sketch (for example, "Dodecahedron—Net 1;" "Dodecahedron—Net 2").

Preparing for the Closing

4. Determine whether each net diagram is the net of a prism or of a pyramid. Say how you know.

a. 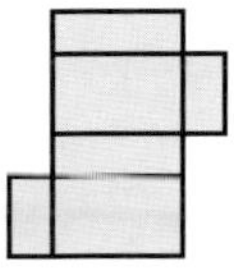

b. 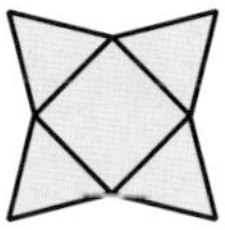

c. 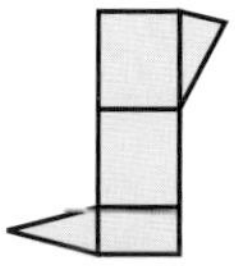

d. 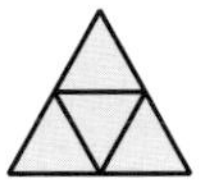

Skills

A shirt is sold for a price of $20. What would be its new price if:

a. The price is increased by 25%

b. The price is decreased by 25%

c. The shirt is sold at 25% off

d. You increase the price by 25% and then decrease the new price by 25%

Review and Consolidation

Here are some familiar solids.

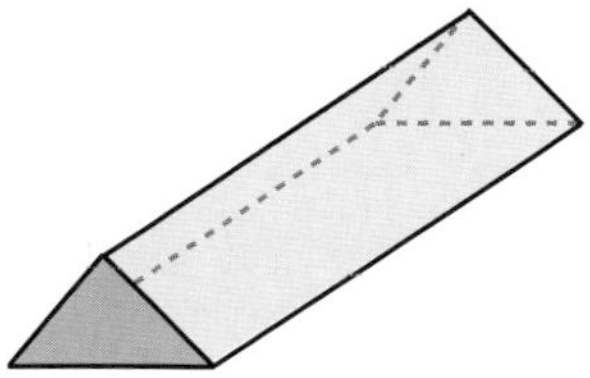

triangular prism

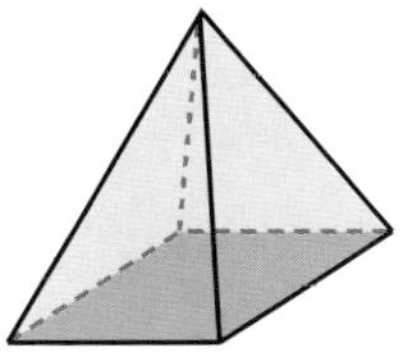

square pyramid

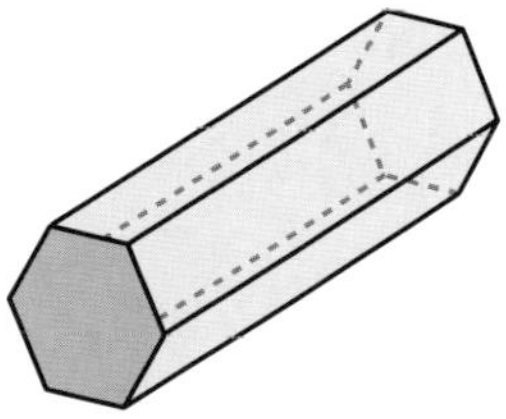

hexagonal prism

One method for making nets of shapes like these is to draw around each face on a sheet of paper. This is called the *rolling method*.

For the pentagonal prism, you would draw around the first face, as shown right.

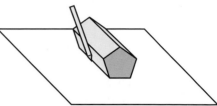

Then you would roll the prism over and draw around the next face, then roll and draw again.

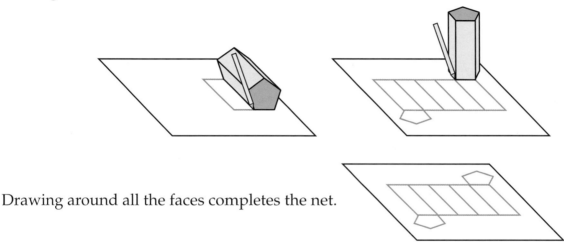

Drawing around all the faces completes the net.

Your teacher will provide you with a set of solids. Use the rolling method to create nets of the solids as described below.

1. Nets of parallel solids

- Take out two prisms from the set of solids.
- On a large sheet of blank paper, draw a net for each shape by rolling. (Make sure you only draw around each face once.)
- Create a different net by rolling the shape a different way. Write the name of each shape under each net and label the two nets "Net 1" and "Net 2."

2. Nets of point solids

- Take out five pyramids from the set of solids.
- On a large sheet of blank paper, draw a net for each shape by rolling. (Make sure you only draw around each face once.)
- Create a different net by rolling the shape a different way. Write the name of each shape under each net and label the two nets "Net 1" and "Net 2."

Homework

1. Here are some net diagrams. **A** and **C** are the nets of a tetrahedron and the others are not. Say why.

A

B

C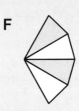

D

E

F

2. On grid paper, draw the net diagrams of the solids shown in the figures below.

a.

b.

To learn how to make oblique drawings on a two-dimensional grid.

Oblique Drawings

Oblique means sloping neither vertically nor horizontally. Oblique drawings show one of the dimensions of a figure angled at 45°. Note that lines of equal length do not always appear equal in oblique drawings.

Example

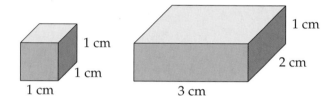

To make oblique drawings, you need to use oblique grid paper.

Start by drawing the front of the shape.

Add the sides and tops of the objects, angled at 45° to the horizontal following these steps:

- Draw the angled depth dimension in a special way. For each measurement of 1 unit, draw the angled line along half the diagonal of one square of the grid paper. Shortening the depth in this way makes drawings look more realistic.

- Then, complete the drawings by adding the missing back and side edges.

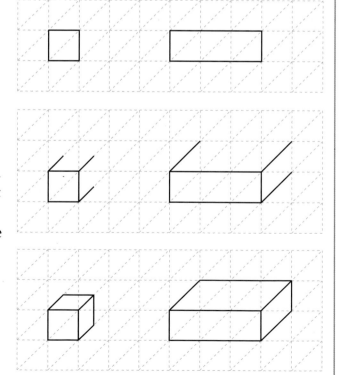

Work Time

1. a. Copy and complete this oblique drawing
   of a rectangular prism.

   b. What are the dimensions of the solid?

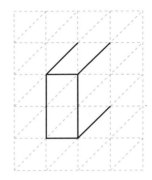

2. a. Copy and complete this oblique drawing
   of a rectangular prism.

   b. What are the dimensions of the solid?

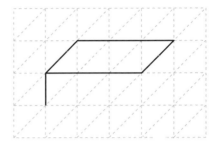

3. Show all of the steps needed to make an oblique drawing for each of these figures.

a.

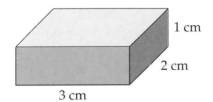

1 cm
2 cm
3 cm

b.

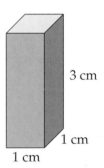

3 cm
1 cm
1 cm

c.

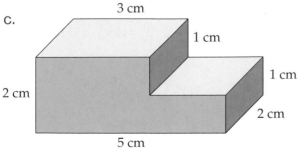

3 cm
1 cm
1 cm
2 cm
2 cm
5 cm

d.

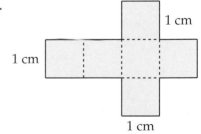

1 cm
1 cm
1 cm

4. Build these shapes with wooden cubes; then, draw them on oblique grid paper. Use a scale in which the side of one cube is shown as one square on the drawing.

a.

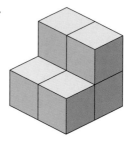

b.

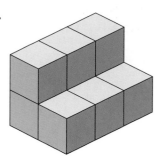

Preparing for the Closing

5. Sit directly opposite your partner with a table between you.

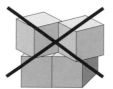

a. Work together to build a figure out of wooden cubes.

   Make sure that your construction joins with all faces lining up at right angles or straight angles.

b. Now each of you should draw how you see the figure from your side of the table on oblique grid paper.

c. Discuss your results with your partner. Were your drawings the same? Why or why not?

Skills

Represent each statement as a decimal and as a fraction.

   a. A price, p, is increased by 10%.

   b. A price, p, is decreased by 10%.

   c. A price, p, is increased by 20%.

   d. A price, p, is decreased by 1%.

Review and Consolidation

1. a. Copy and complete this oblique drawing of a rectangular prism.

   b. What are the dimensions of the solid?

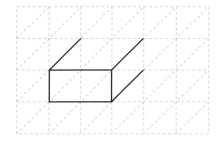

2. a. Copy and complete this oblique drawing of a rectangular prism.

   b. What are the dimensions of the solid?

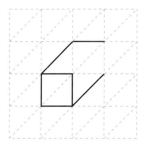

3. Show all of the steps needed to make an oblique drawing for each of these figures.

a.

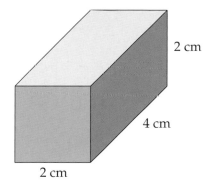

b.

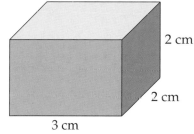

c.

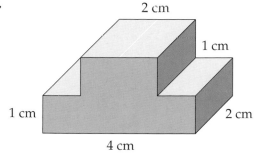

d.

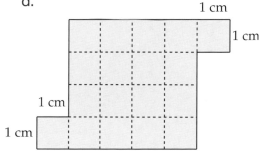

4. Make a building of your own design from wooden cubes. Make sure that your construction joins with all faces lining up at right angles or straight angles.

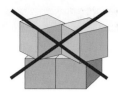

a. Make an oblique drawing of your building.

b. Make another drawing of your building, viewed from a different side.

c. Make another drawing of your building, viewed from another side.

Homework

1. a. Copy and complete this oblique drawing of a rectangular prism.

b. What are the dimensions of the solid?

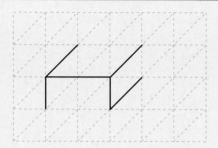

2. a. Copy and complete this oblique drawing of a rectangular prism.

b. What are the dimensions of the solid?

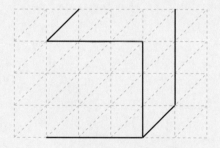

3. Show all of the steps needed to make an oblique drawing for each of these figures.

a.

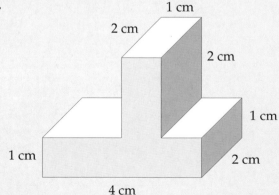

1 cm
2 cm
2 cm
1 cm
1 cm
2 cm
4 cm

b.

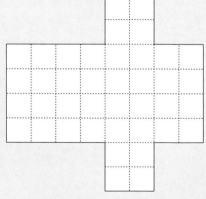

COMPARING THREE-DIMENSIONAL DRAWINGS

GOAL

To learn how to make isometric drawings on a two-dimensional grid, and to compare oblique, orthogonal, and isometric drawings.

Isometric Drawings

Isometric means "equal measure." In isometric drawings, equal lines look equal. Isometric drawings show sloping edges drawn at 30° to the horizontal.

Example

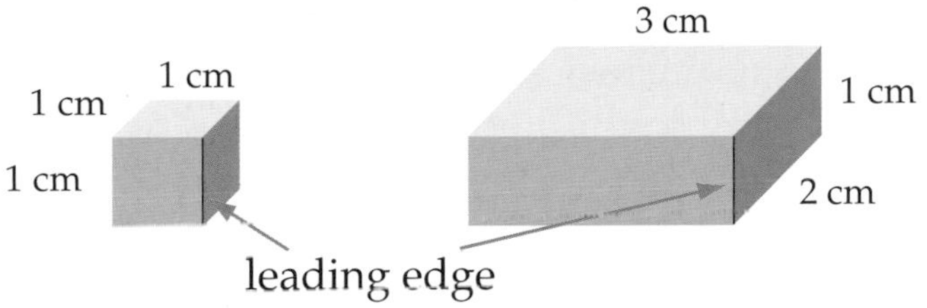

1 cm
1 cm
1 cm

3 cm
1 cm
2 cm

leading edge

Start by drawing the leading edge.

Next, draw the sloping edges.

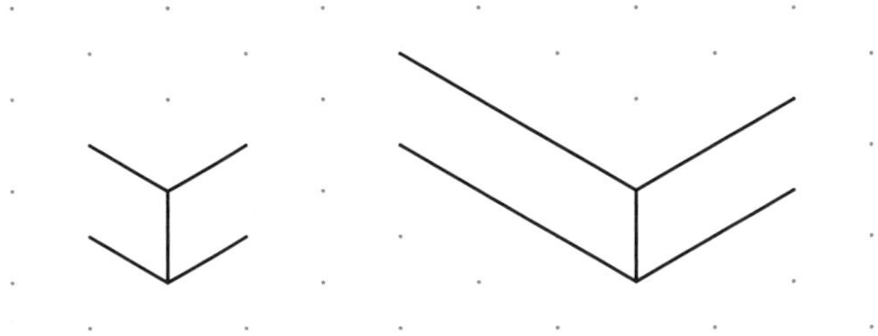

Draw the remaining lines needed to complete the drawing, as shown.

Then shade the surfaces lying in parallel planes in the same way. Shading gives a proper three-dimensional look to the drawing.

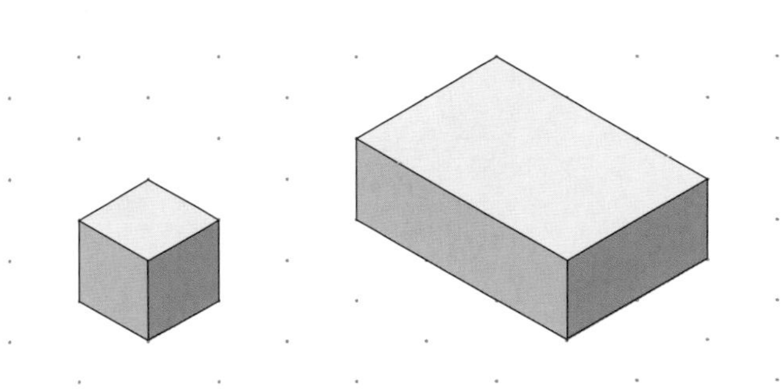

Here are some more examples of isometric drawings.

── Example ──────────────────────

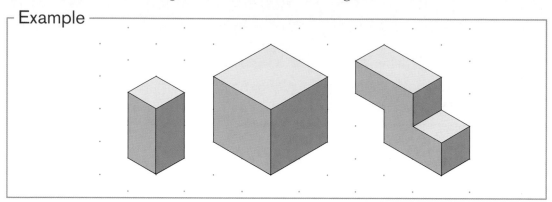

Orthogonal Drawings

Orthogonal drawings are two-dimensional representations of three-dimensional shapes. The three different views (front, side, and top) are different elevations or perspectives of the three-dimensional object.

── Example ──────────────────────

Imagine you walk around this three-dimensional object.

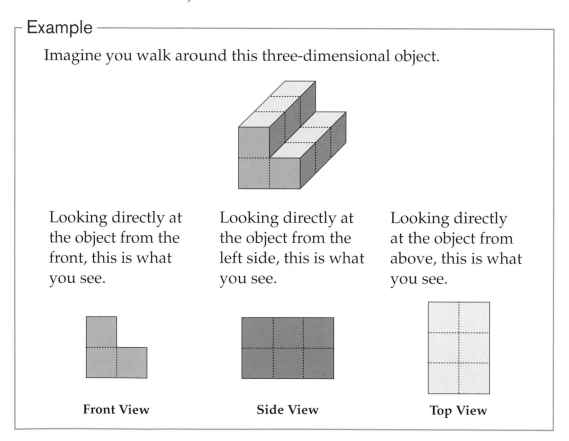

Looking directly at the object from the front, this is what you see.

Looking directly at the object from the left side, this is what you see.

Looking directly at the object from above, this is what you see.

Front View   **Side View**   **Top View**

Four Ways of Drawing Three-Dimensional Objects

You have learned about four different ways of representing three-dimensional objects in a two-dimensional drawing.

Nets	A net is a two-dimensional shape that can fold up to form a three-dimensional object. A net is a plan of a three-dimensional solid. Nets are drawn so that edges touch along their lengths.	
Oblique Drawings	Oblique means sloping neither vertically nor horizontally. Oblique drawings show one of the dimensions of a figure angled at 45°. In oblique drawings, lines of equal length do not always appear equal. To make oblique drawings, we use oblique grid paper.	
Isometric Drawings	Isometric means equal (*iso*) measure (*metric*), so lines of equal length appear equal. Isometric drawings have sloping edges drawn at 30°. To make isometric drawings, we use isometric dot or grid paper.	
Orthogonal Drawings	In orthogonal drawings you represent the way a figure looks viewed from the front, the side, and the top.	Front Side Top

Work Time

1. Use isometric dot paper to make isometric drawings for each of these figures.

   a.

   b.

   c.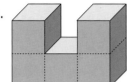

   d.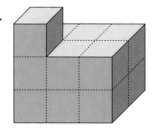

2. Use oblique grid paper to make oblique drawings for each of the solids in these orthogonal drawings.

	Front	**Right Side**	**Top**
a.			
b.			

3. Make orthogonal front, right-side, and top drawings for each of the solids in these isometric drawings. Make sure to label your drawings with the correct sides.

   a.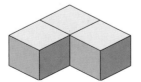

   b.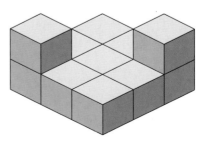

Preparing for the Closing

4. An oblique drawing puts more emphasis on the front of a three-dimensional shape, whereas an isometric drawing puts more focus on the edge of an object. To achieve this, the sides are angled differently.

   a. What degree angle do oblique drawings usually use?

   b. What degree angle do isometric drawings usually use?

5. Compare oblique and isometric grid paper. What is the same? What is different? Include both angles and lines in your answer.

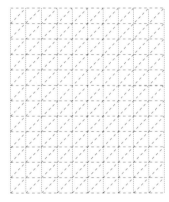

Oblique Grid

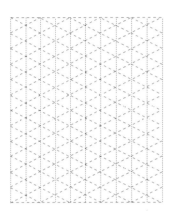

Isometric Grid

Comment

You have been using isometric dot paper. Isometric grid paper is the same with lines drawn between the dots.

Skills

Lisa added and subtracted these numbers and then copied the answers onto another piece of paper. She noticed that she forgot to copy the decimal points in the answers.

Where should she add the decimal points?

a. $2.5 + 3625 = 36275$

b. $212.5 + 42.17 = 25467$

c. $212.5 - 42.17 = 17033$

d. $1583 - 1203 = 380$

e. $2563 + 27.7 = 25907$

f. $7852 - 253.6 = 75984$

Review and Consolidation

1. Consider this net of a three-dimensional shape.

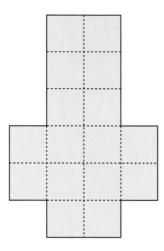

   a. Make an oblique drawing of the figure using the oblique grid paper.

   b. Make an isometric drawing of the figure using the isometric dot paper.

   c. Make orthogonal front, right-side, and top drawings for the figure.

2. Consider this oblique drawing of a three-dimensional shape.

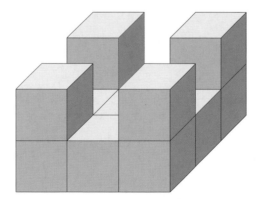

   a. Make an isometric drawing of the figure using isometric dot paper.

   b. Make orthogonal front, right-side, and top drawings for the figure.

1. Use isometric dot paper to make isometric drawings for each of these figures.

a.

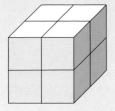

b.

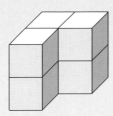

2. Use oblique grid paper to make oblique drawings for each of these figures.

a.

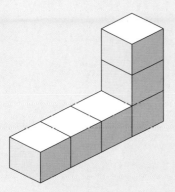

b.

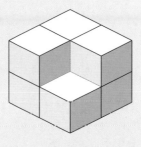

3. Make orthogonal front, right-side, and top drawings for each of these solids with isometric views. Make sure to label your drawings with the correct sides.

a.

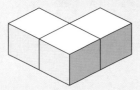

b.

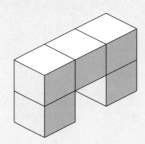

GOAL

To calculate the girth, surface area, and volume of a sphere.

Lisa, Rosa, Jamal, Dwayne, and Chen were throwing a baseball in Dwayne's backyard.

Jamal threw the ball to Dwayne, who caught it and said, "Hey! I just realized that a ball is an example of a sphere."

"Yes," agreed Chen, catching the ball. "We learned in class that *spheres* are round, three-dimensional objects."

Chen threw the ball to Rosa, who continued on the subject of spheres like she was quoting from the textbook. "Yes, and the *diameter* of a sphere is a line segment with endpoints on the surface of the sphere that intersects the center of the sphere."

She threw the ball to Lisa who also continued like she was quoting the book. "The *girth* of a sphere is the circumference around its center."

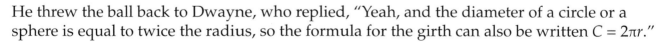

Jamal caught the ball. "Hey, this is fun! Girth is calculated using the formula $C = \pi d$, where d is the diameter of the sphere."

He threw the ball back to Dwayne, who replied, "Yeah, and the diameter of a circle or a sphere is equal to twice the radius, so the formula for the girth can also be written $C = 2\pi r$."

"You can also use the radius to calculate the surface area and volume of a sphere using the formulas $S = 4\pi r^2$ and $V = \dfrac{4}{3}\pi r^3$," finished Chen, dropping the ball and lying down on the grass. "I am exhausted," he sighed. "Game over."

CONCEPT BOOK

See pages 235–236, 238–240, 245, 251, and 254.

Example

The radius of a ball is $1\frac{1}{4}$ inches.

The diameter of the ball is $2\frac{1}{2}$ inches.

The circumference of the ball is: $C = 2\pi r$

$\approx 2(3.14) \bullet 1.25$

$\approx 6.28 \bullet 1.25$

≈ 7.85 in (inches)

(or you can round your answer to $C = 7.9$ inches)

The surface area of the ball is: $S = 4\pi r^2$

$= 4\pi \bullet 1.25^2$

$\approx 4(3.14)(1.25)(1.25)$

≈ 19.625 in^2 (square inches)

The volume of the ball is: $V = \frac{4}{3}\pi r^3$

$= \frac{4}{3}\pi(1.25)^3$

$\approx 1.\overline{3} \bullet 3.14 \bullet 1.953125$

≈ 8.18 in^3 (cubic inches)

Work Time

Use a calculator for these problems.

1. Lisa is decorating a spherical holiday ornament of diameter 3 inches. What length of ribbon will she need to wrap around the girth of the ornament? (Express your answer in terms of π.)

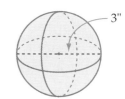

2. Use the $\boxed{\pi}$ button on your calculator. This basketball has a diameter of 24 cm.

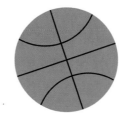

   a. Calculate the surface area.

   b. Calculate the volume.

Work with a partner for problems 3 and 4.

3. Chen is buying a fish tank. He has the choice of two tanks: a rectangular prism or a tank in the shape of a *hemisphere* (half of a sphere). Which tank will give his fish the most space in which to swim?

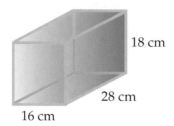

18 cm

28 cm

16 cm

←—— 32 cm ——→

4. A domed roof is being built over a circular swimming pool. It must have a diameter of 90 m. What will be the surface area of the new roof?

Preparing for the Closing

5. Compare your answers for problems 3 and 4 with another pair of students.

   • Did all of you calculate the same measurements for each problem?

   • Discuss which words in the problems led you to make the calculations you did.

   • Did the figures in problem 3 help you make decisions?

   • Was it useful to sketch your own figure for either of the problems?

6. What information about a sphere can you calculate if you know the measure of the radius or diameter?

7. Jamal, Rosa, and Lisa each attempted to measure the diameter of a ball before calculating its volume.

   Jamal measured the diameter of the ball as 6 cm.
   Rosa measured the diameter and decided it was 7 cm.
   Lisa decided that the best value to use for the diameter of the ball was 6.5 cm.

   To calculate the volume of the ball, all three students decided to use the $\boxed{\pi}$ button on their calculators and round their answers to two decimal places.

   How did their answers for the volume compare? Use your results to write about how the accuracy of the direct measurement affected the calculated measure.

Skills

Lisa multiplied and divided these numbers and then copied the answers onto another piece of paper. She noticed that she forgot to copy the decimal points in the answers.

Where should she place the decimal point in each answer?

a. 43.75 • 125 = 546875   b. 125 ÷ 2.5 = 500   c. 6.25 • 1.5 = 9375

d. 23.7 • 4.27 = 101199   e. 14,656 ÷ 32 = 4580   f. 12.5 • 1346 = 168250

Review and Consolidation

1. Calculate the girth, surface area, and volume of a golf ball of radius 20 mm. (Use the $\boxed{\pi}$ button on your calculator and round all answers to one decimal place.)

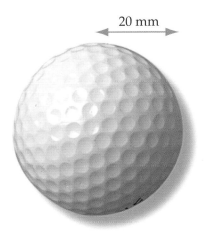

20 mm

2. A hemispherical bowl has a diameter of 12 cm. What is its volume? Give your answer in terms of π.

12 cm

Homework

1. Which of these shapes has the larger girth?

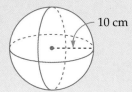 A

 B

2. Calculate the surface area of this sphere. Write your answer in terms of π.

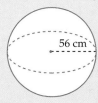

3. Calculate the volume of each shape. Write your answers in terms of π.

a.

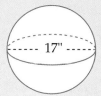

b.

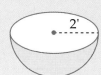

To apply the concepts of geometry and measure.

Distances along, around, or across are one-dimensional, or linear, measures. *Linear units* are used for one-dimensional measures.

CONCEPT BOOK

See pages 249–254.

The linear measures you have been studying are *length, width, height, radius, diameter, perimeter, circumference*, and *girth*. These measurements can be made on one-, two-, or three-dimensional figures.

Area and *surface area* are two-dimensional measures. These measures are the result of multiplying two linear measures. *Square units* are used for these measurements.

Area can be measured on two-dimensional shapes. Surface area is the measure of the total area on the surface of three-dimensional objects.

Volume is a three-dimensional measure. It is the result of either multiplying three linear measures or multiplying a two-dimensional measure by a one-dimensional measure. *Cubic units* are used for these measurements.

Volume can be measured only for three-dimensional objects.

One-Dimensional Measure (Linear Units)		Two-Dimensional Measure (Square Units)	Three-Dimensional Measure (Cubic Units)
Length	Radius		
Width	Diameter	Area	Volume
Height	Circumference	Surface Area	
Perimeter	Girth		

Putting Mathematics to Work

Work Time

Use a calculator with a $\boxed{\pi}$ button for these problems.

1. Concrete grain silos on a farm are used to protect grain from the sun and rain.

Their shape is shown in the figure.

a. What is the outside radius of the silo?

b. What is the inside radius of the silo?

c. What volume of concrete is needed to build one of these silos assuming the wall has a thickness of 50 cm?

d. What volume of grain can one silo store?

e. The local farmers harvest 100,000 m³ of grain. How many silos are needed to store their grain?

Concrete Grain Silo

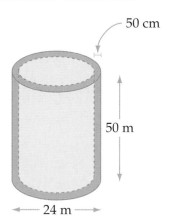

50 cm

50 m

24 m

2. Mr. Peterson, the principal at Monroe High School, has to make a choice between two new logos for a banner. Each design is based on parts of circles.

In order to save production costs, Mr. Peterson will choose the logo with the least area. Which one should he choose? Justify your answer.

Logo 1

Logo 2

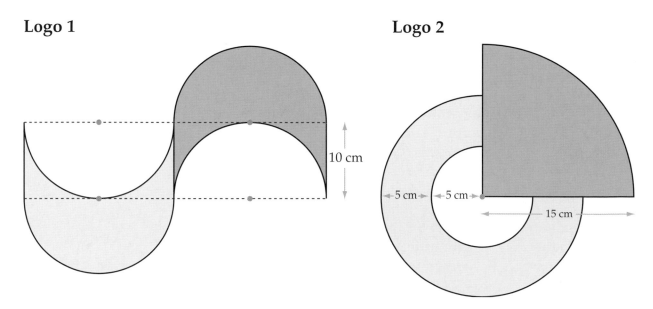

10 cm

5 cm 5 cm 15 cm

Putting Mathematics to Work

Preparing for the Closing

3. Discuss your solutions to the Work Time problems with your partner and then with another pair of students.

- Compare your solutions. Did you use the same methods to solve each of the problems? If not, how did your methods differ?

- Do you think that everyone should necessarily obtain the same answers and the same areas for the logos in problem 2? Explain your response.

Water flowed into a tank for 8 minutes.
The line shows the volume of water in the tank during this time.

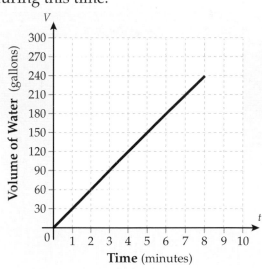

a. How long did it take to add 60 gallons?

b. How many gallons of water were added to the tank in 6 minutes?

c. How many gallons of water were added to the tank in 7 minutes?

d. How many gallons of water were added to the tank in $6\frac{1}{2}$ minutes?

e. How many gallons of water were added to the tank per minute?

Putting Mathematics to Work

Review and Consolidation

1. a. A farmer owns a farm in the shape of a rectangle, shown at right.

What is the area of the farm?

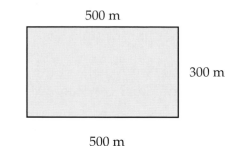
500 m
300 m

b. A neighbor sells the farmer an adjacent piece of land in the shape of a triangle.

What is the area of the farm now?

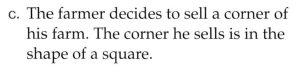
500 m
300 m
300 m

c. The farmer decides to sell a corner of his farm. The corner he sells is in the shape of a square.

What is the area of the farm now?

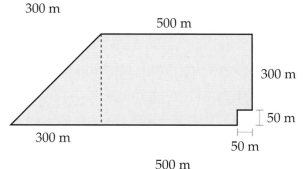
500 m
300 m
50 m
50 m
300 m

d. The farmer is able to buy land in the shape of a large triangle on the southern border of his farm.

What is the area of the farm now?

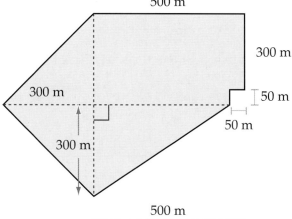
500 m
300 m
300 m
50 m
50 m
300 m
300 m

e. The farmer gives the darkly shaded region of his farm to his daughter.

How much land does his daughter receive?

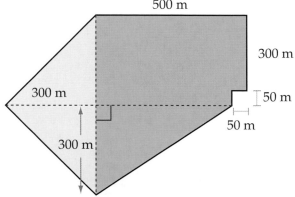
500 m
300 m
50 m
50 m
300 m
300 m
300 m

Homework

1. a. Calculate the circumference of the base of this cylinder.

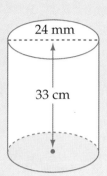

b. Calculate the area of the base.

c. Calculate the volume of the cylinder.

d. Suppose a cone has the same size base and the same volume.
What would be the height of the cone?

e. Calculate the height of a box with the same volume
as the cylinder and a base that is 16 mm × 25 mm.

Putting Mathematics to Work

Page numbers in red are found in the *Concept Book.*

Page numbers in red are found in the *Concept Book*.

Page numbers in red are found in the *Concept Book.*

Page numbers in red are found in the *Concept Book*.